A STUDIO PRESS BOOK

First published in the UK in 2020 by Studio Press,
an imprint of Bonnier Books UK,
The Plaza, 535 King's Road, London SW10 0SZ
Owned by Bonnier Books,
Sveavägen 56, Stockholm, Sweden

www.studiopressbooks.co.uk
www.bonnierbooks.co.uk

Artwork © Amandeep Singh 2020
Editorial © Eleanor Penny and Tom MacAndrew 2020
Ike/Rust text © Inua Ellams 2020
Voices from East of the Sun, West of the Moon text © Helen Mort 2020
A Bluebeard Among the Blue Birds text © Joelle Taylor 2020
Nyaminyami text © Kayo Chingonyi 2020
Moon Station 5 text © Will Harris 2020
The Making of a Dwen text © Malika Booker 2020

1 3 5 7 9 10 8 6 4 2

ISBN 978-1-78741-772-4

Edited by Tom MacAndrew, Eleanor Penny, Frankie Jones and Helen Wicks
Designed by Rob Ward
Production by Emma Kidd

MIX
Paper from
responsible sources
FSC
www.fsc.org
FSC® C009279

A CIP catalogue for this book is available from the British Library

Printed and bound in Spain.

INK
TALES

BEDTIME STORIES FOR THE END OF THE WORLD

About Bedtime Stories for the End of the World

About The Poets

About Inkquisitive

INTRODUCTION

When Sheherezade wanted to placate the tyrant king Shahryar – to save her life, and the life of her sister – she would distract him with tantalising stories of magic and adventure, never quite finishing the tale. If he killed her, the king would never find out how the story ended – something he could never quite bring himself to do.

Today, teams of artists and scientists are trying to figure out a way to warn future generations about the lingering threat from the nuclear waste we have barrelled and buried under the earth. One suggestion is to breed a species of cat whose fur would change colour in the presence of nuclear radiation, and release them into the wild around disposal sites. Then we would sow myths and legends which caution that if you see a feline creature shifting colours, you turn and you run.

What we mean to say is that stories can be a way to survive.

In the ancient Greek epic poem *The Odyssey*, King Odysseus' ship is blown far off course. He lands on a small wooded island where he and his men are caught by a Cyclops, a giant man with one eye set squarely in the middle of his face. On the island of Crete, archeologists recently discovered the skull of a wooly mammoth. They speculated that the ancient Greeks might also have

stumbled across these vast, fossilised remains. The skull of a woolly mammoth has a hole set squarely in the middle, where a trunk – or perhaps, an eye – would once have been.

In the hot summer of 1518, the people of Strasbourg began to dance. It started with one woman, jigging and shaking in the town square. More and more joined her, their numbers swelling to a crowd of hundreds who danced without stopping for days on end. Some of them collapsed and died of exhaustion. The authorities soon began to blame the 'dancing plague' on a holy wrath visited on a sinful population. They swiftly banned music and dancing, and introduced a strict period of enforced public penance. The surviving dancers were given red shoes to cover their bloodied feet, and led off into the hills to the shrine of St Vitus, the patron saint of dancers. In Grimm's 1812 version of *Snow White*, the evil queen is cursed to dance in red hot shoes until she drops dead. Today, the neurological disorder Syndenham's chorea, which causes the limbs to jerk uncontrollably, is sometimes known as 'St Vitus' dance'.

What we mean to say is that what survives of us is stories.

When civilisations fall, when the buildings

have crumbled to rubble and the people have gone, there are still monstrous women beckoning travellers into the river, and half-god tricksters wrestling snakes on a bare mountain at night. When floods sweep cities underwater, stories buoy up to the surface of the waves. When people are chased from their homes, they carry their stories on their backs with them like children.

In 2017, we started the podcast 'Bedtime Stories for the End of the World', to investigate what kind of stories we want to pass on to future generations; which myths, legends and fairy stories we want to preserve from flood, fire, war, or human forgetfulness. Chaotic and extraordinary times can be just the right moment to ask what parts of the past we want to carry with us, and how the stories we tell each other can build a better future.

This book takes up that mission again, with six of the UK's top writers selecting a favourite tale to preserve within these pages. We're excited to bring you stories from Malika Booker, Will Harris, Helen Mort, Inua Ellams, Kayo Chingonyi and Joelle Taylor – all brought to life by the dreamy, hypnotic illustrations of world-famous artist Inkquisitive.

Our writers spent time rummaging in the rubble discarded by previous generations, exploring unexpected avenues and unsung characters of familiar tales, and sometimes salvaging stories purposefully tossed onto the bonfires of history. This is all par for the course when it comes to spinning a story. Most myths were sung and recited for hundreds of years before they were ever written down, which is to say, that all tellings have always been retellings.

In this heady, bewildering process, things change, shift, are misheard or forgotten, filled-in and questioned, as people explore the meaning of what they had been told – and wonder which parts of it they want to pass on. When all tellings are retellings, we find a lot of possibilities to explore. We can wonder what happens when Philoctetes arrives on Moon Station 5, and can listen in to hear the gin-soaked voice of the wicked stepmother, smoking out of the bedroom window.

In this book, the spirits of unborn children haunt the living, and a snake-headed river god lingers in the waters of the Zambezi. A modern-day Icarus earns her wings in a refugee camp. Bear-brides are taken from the houses of their fathers and mothers quietly by night; a lonely girl tangles with a sinister blue-bearded tyrant; and ancient Greek heroes sing new war anthems in the outermost reaches of space. The stories span several continents and thousands of years – but they talk the same language of hope, grief and courage, of growing up and letting go, of turmoil, discovery and adventure. A language we hope survives onwards as you begin your tellings and retellings of these stories.

– Eleanor Penny & Tom MacAndrew, June 2020

Ike/Rust

Inua Ellams

Ike/Rust

Inua Ellams

The myth of Icarus in its simplest moralisation, is about the dangers of hubris. In the original story, Icarus is the son of the master craftsman, Daedalus. They attempt to escape from the island of Crete with wings Daedalus has constructed from feathers and wax. Daedalus warns Icarus of complacency and arrogance, asking him not to fly too low that the sea's dampness might clog his wings, or too high that the sun's heat might melt them. Icarus ignores his father's instructions and flies too close to the sun. When the wax in his wings melts, he tumbles out of the sky and falls into the sea where he drowns.

I grew up on comic books, where stories of flight left an indelible mark on me. I'd see Iron Man, Storm, Angel or Magneto take to the skies and wish I could be among their number. Of all the heroes, of all their distinct and complicated personalities, Spiderman also known as Peter Parker felt the closest to me. Like him, I was a bespectacled nerd, a creative child, a maker of things. When I poured over the various editions of his epic sagas, the morals and lessons that underpinned his adventures came from his father figure, Uncle Ben. He warned Peter, "With great power, comes great responsibility".

Peter, as an inventor, was both Daedalus and Icarus, making web-shooters, testing them out, learning the repercussions of flying too close to the sun, yet always saving himself and those around him before the sea could claim their lives. Spiderman's spirit, his humour and wit had a striking similarity with Anansi, a figure from West African folklore, who is half-spider, half-man. Marvel, who created the figure of Spiderman went as far as folding Anansi into the Marvel Universe, ascribing to him the mantel of the first Spiderman. Anansi is also said to be the keeper of all stories, and all this was playing on my mind when I began working on an interpretation.

I left Nigeria in 1996 and spent the next 15 years shuffling between Dublin and London, fighting for the right to live and work in Europe, in an endless cycle of immigration battles against the incompetent British Home Office. Though my battles continue, all I have suffered pales in comparison to the plight of other immigrants trapped in refugee camps in Sudan, abandoned in the Sahara desert as they tried to reach Libya, left floating in lifeboats on the Mediterranean, and stranded on islands off the coast of Italy. I wanted to write an adaptation that honoured their journey. I wondered who would be stranded in today's world? Who would need to fly? What would stop them? What would push them towards the skies? I found clear answers: refugees. Those who cannot cross water. Litigation and law. Death beneath the water's surface. The biggest change for me was the moral element. I didn't want to debate whether or not refugees had a right to the pursuit of happiness. As an immigrant, it is difficult to be objective, to see this from both sides. I didn't want to wave a finger at my readers. Instead, I wanted to put a beating heart at the centre and explain the complicated world around her. Icarus became the rusty-haired, mischievous girl, Ikenna.

This is her story.

The refugee camp was a battered rainbow of humanity.
Each tent a failing flailing nation's flag weighed down
by stones. The wind would lift sand grains and dust wisps
off the central tent and blow them down the sandy paths
to the edges of the island, the beach, where the refugees
would gather to look across the deep blue waters,
through clouds drifting like slow white whales.

On clear days, they'd see their dream destination, Italy,
freedom, and their dream killers: coastguards, sharks
in water, fast metal boats ruling the seas and
watchtowers on Italian cliffs, watching the hopeful
refugees, warnings clear: to stay put, there, stay
and never leave.

On dark days, those among them who had braved
treacherous waves at night, who carved makeshift boats
from trees to ride the moon-tide's watery cliffs,
the waves would wash back their bodies, their eyes gone
to hungry fish. The men would bury, the women hum,
both forge sweltering songs of sorrow, hardship, pain, loss.

At sundown, the adults would trudge back
for the tasks of keeping home: farms to tend,
tents to sweep. Teenagers would split in couples,
search for huddled copses of trees, to shelter and see
to teenage needs, but the kids would roam free.

This kid, they called Rust. Her hair was a bush of clumps,
her gaze stiff as stumps and among kids of the island
the strong ones, the beautiful, musically gifted, the sprinters,
cry-babies, she was the brave one. Everything an adventure,

she'd dig through landfills that lined the island seeking
gifts of clumped goods, fist-sized bits of clockwork
metal she'd scurry back to her father's workshop,
a scorched tent where he made repairs or tinkered
with his engineering head. The camp dwellers always
brought work, and as Malik fixed their phones or radios,
candles flickering like small gods, they'd talk of their lives
back home, who they once were, what they gave up.
Rust would watch wide-eyed as he worked, suck up
all she could of his skill, nose-dive into landfills looking
to build her works. Unless a worthy distraction appeared,
nothing stopped her search. Today, this was it:
A small cart. Four wheels. Clear path. Down hill.
Back wind. An audience. The thrill.

North of the island. Salma, Rust's mother, leaves
the communal kitchen carrying food for her family:
Malik, his brother, her roughneck daughter. In the tent,
she rises before the spread, spots the clock: dinner time
and bellows her child's name
– Ikenna! Ikenna! Ike...

Rust rushes through the tent's entrance, dishevelled,
bits of dry bush cascading off her like rotting confetti.
Her mother bellows louder
 – Have you been climbing landfill again?
    You are covered in rust! Sand in your hair?
    You wounded? Cut! Child, is that blood?!
– Mamma don't worry, I've suffered worse
– The women laugh at the child I've got
    who will never get…
– Married? Mamma, I work better alone,
    I don't need to get married!

Rust hurries off as Salma carries on. Malik enters
– Is my brother here?

They hug, a brief tight clinch in which an essay
worth of words pass
– Gone since breakfast, you saw him last
– Maybe he'll come after dinner. Is Ikenna here?
– Coming
Rust says, rushing, her hair a bush half tamed.

Night squats over the camp. Storytellers gather.
Musicians strum. Thirst is quenched. Bellies swell
till silence and sleep claim them again.

Morning. The sun, frozen in the sky. Winged insects
dapple by, a hurried voice at the tent's mouth
– Malik, it's your brother, come quick.

They found him washed up on the shore, whatever craft
the waves had bore, how far he'd gotten, what he saw,
knowledge he could share of the world beyond, locked
in his body, his eyes gone. Malik crumples to the shore
and when the burial is done, songs sung, the camp as one
turns inland, but Rust stands, kicks the sand,
her eyes a stump of darkness.

She heads south, picking her way through shallow
rock pools, starfish, mussels, crabs, stops before
a camouflaged cave, checks she isn't followed and ducks
into her hideaway. The walls are papered every which way
with charcoal sketches of pulleys and levers, clockwork,
etches of feathered motors. Rust lights a candle, hoists it
high above her head, pours light over a full-sized model
she hopes will cross the sea. Rust kneels before
her scrapheap wings, thinking of his life, says

– Uncle, it will fly. Tomorrow, you'll see.

Dawn. Rust, who worked through the night slips back
to her tent, a somber assortment of compassionate,
merciful mourners who camouflaged her absence.
Salma stops her only child
– You hungry? You eaten?
   Ikenna, did you sleep?
Rust shrugs and struggles out
her grip, ruffles among her things for nuts, spare screws
and bolts back to her cave. At noon she steps out,
the wings strapped to her back, and walks the busy path
through the refugee camp, crowds trailing, questions
about the mouths

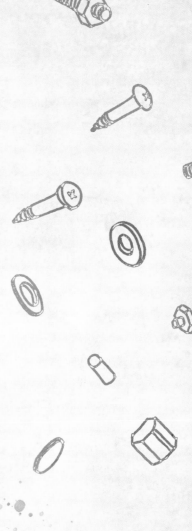

– What is she doing? What do you think?
   Do you think that thing will fly?
   We've to leave this island, otherwise we'll die.
   But isn't that dangerous?

Rust stops

– I must try. Tell my parents I'm going to the highest
   rocky cliff. Updrafts should help the lift-off
   and the wind should glide me clean past
   the rocks and by the time they reach the beach,
   I should be halfway crossed to Italy, the dream.

At first, the Italian coastguards ignore the large bird,
but for the metallic glint that sheens among its feathers
they lean into their telescopes
– Captain, it's a girl! She must have left the island
– Don't be absurd

He spits out his stiff drink and radios the snipers
– Is that a girl flying? Confirm what I see?

Back on the island, the refugees thrill as Rust swoops
through the sky, mastering the wind. Malik calls
– Ikenna! Fly! Straight to Italy!

The kids chant
– Rust! Ikenna! Rust! Ikenna

breeze takes their chants and calls
like prayers to her wings and on she flies to Italy,
to freedom in their dreams.

When the first bolt pops, Rust doesn't scream.
When the harness belt snaps, she steadies in the wind.
When a wing tears off, doubt slashes at that dream.
And the second wing pulls her down beneath the sea.
Silence takes the refugees, they stand, solemn, stone-still.
Malik, staring where she fell, Salma not daring to breathe,
the folks deepening in sorrow that the sea had claimed
their kin, had added to the souls oceans already keep.

The refugees search for the right mournful hymn
but as their mouths form words, Salma's hushes them.
– My daughter accomplished an incredible thing,
   she flew and reached for a future she could barely see.
   Brave, unstoppable, unmatched in zeal, when you sing
   her story, keep her bright, keep her real.

Voices from East of the Sun, West of the Moon

Helen Mort

VOICES FROM EAST OF THE SUN, WEST OF THE MOON

Helen Mort

East of the Sun and West of the Moon is an old Norwegian fairy tale, collected by Peter Christen Asbjørnsen and Jørgen Moe. It is a quest narrative, a great adventure. It's also a story of an unusual marriage. It involves shapeshifting, transformation, loss and reunion – its twists and turns keep the reader on their toes and that's one of the reasons I was drawn to it.

If I had to summarise the plot simply (and I can't), I'd say something like this: a young girl is sold by her parents to a white bear who wants to marry her. They share a bed every night but she never sees him. One day, she lights candles and reveals his true form: a handsome prince. But in seeing him, she breaks the spell – he's been cursed by his wicked stepmother into the form of a bear. Now that the girl has seen him, he's doomed to go back to the stepmother's castle and marry her ugly daughter, a troll princess. But the girl is determined to rescue him and makes the difficult journey to the place he's held captive, a mysterious castle East of the Sun and West of the Moon.

As a poet who loves climbing and running, I'm used to writing about the specific features of landscapes, rocks and streams and maps and co-ordinates. I was drawn to the idea of a castle with no tangible location, a place nearly impossible to find. I also love the idea of an arduous quest – in the story, the girl has to plead with the wind to carry her there. Once she arrives, she still has to bargain and scheme just to get near to her lover. When she finally reaches him,

they cook up a plot together. It's a bit like the glass slipper in *Cinderella* – the prince says he'll promise to marry anyone who can clean the drops of candle wax from his shirt, knowing that the girl is the only one who will be able to do it.

As with most fairy tales, there are many aspects of *East of the Sun and West of the Moon* that might make a modern audience raise their eyebrows. The girl doesn't have any say in her arranged betrothal to the bear – she's just sold by her father. She accepts her fate, remains completely loyal to the bear (even more so when she finds out he's really a handsome man). And what leads her to her happy ending? Housework, her ability to clean her prince's shirt properly. She's not exactly a liberated figure. And yet she's powerful and independent at the same time, finding her way to the enchanted castle using wit and ingenuity. Nothing's simple in this story and that's why I like it.

I was also very interested in the role of the spell-casting stepmother. More people live in blended families in the UK now than ever before. I'm one of them – I have one child and two step children. When I became a stepmum, I remembered all the wicked stepmothers in fairy tales and films, saw them lining up before me with cartoonish lipstick and talons for fingernails, and cringed. I knew I wanted to give the stepmum in my retelling of the story a distinctive voice, make her a complicated figure, full of contradictions, like all of us.

The Newspaper

I'm the one who inks history.
Each night when I'm tired of being read
I slip outside and turn the pages of the earth,
rifle through the rustling trees, rummage
in the tower blocks, turn over houses
until I find the pieces that I'm looking for.
Tonight, I choose a pretty youngest daughter,
a father who gives her away, a prince
trapped in the body of a polar bear.
I build suspense. I write her curiosity,
the night she sees through the bear-skin
and breaks the spell. I sense a scandal now.
I hook you in. I whisk him to the house
of his wicked stepmother, invent a daughter
to betroth him to. I give her some deformity –
I know what readers want. I send the girl
to search for him. I make it difficult.
I hide him in some small back pocket
of the galaxy, make her bargain
with the wind to travel there. Despite myself,
I end it happily. I stage a test, the girl
arriving just in time, the only one
who knows just how to iron the prince's shirt.
That's it. The end. I don't bother to tidy up
the ugly child, the crinkled bear skin or
the rattling, roaming wind, the step mum
in her quiet room. But listen to me write!
I know what sells. I know what stories
you deserve.

The Mother: *Nobody's interested in mothers. We're in the background, making hot tea and bread. But this is my story too, my life. And it starts like this: once, a White Bear approached a poor peasant, asked for his prettiest, youngest daughter in return for cash. Not just any daughter – my child. She didn't want to go, but she's a girl, she had no voice. And my husband said we needed the money. I stood in the doorway and became liquid, became a river of grief. The bear whisked her away to his castle. I watched their shapes becoming distant stars. I imagined her life with him. At night, he would take off his bear form and come to her bed as a man, but the darkness meant she never saw him. I'd love to know how a bear thinks, what a bear feels.*

The White Bear

I'm cursed into this shape, and now I
curse the blood diamonds of my teeth,
the musk of my scraggy fur. Curse
the muscles underneath, withering.
Curse my death-cudgel paws, knives
of my claws. Curse the memory of seal fat
and how at sunset a rock can look
blubbery as a seal. Curse the rocky
outcrops of hunger, how hunger tightens
like a vice and curse the shifting, splintering
multitudes of ice, how the world
is always softening under me. Curse the men
who drank and drank and drank
from the lip of the earth and yet
left more water, less solid ground.
Curse the surfaces I try to
walk on, unsteady, waiting
to break through, waiting
to break out of this rigid skin.

The Mother: *For weeks, I barely slept. Each dawn, I woke with her name on my lips. I will not share it with you because it is ours, our secret. I imagined her waking in a cool bed, the bear snoring beside her. I sent her letters, folded them into the shape of birds and cast them into the air. I knew they would reach her. I hoped she had someone to speak to, someone to hear what she'd been through. If no one would listen, I hoped she could write it down.*

The Girl

We are taken from the houses of our fathers / mothers quietly
by night. They watch us go, palming the silver / gold. Briefly, they weep.
The heat in the back of the pick up / lorry / jeep is the open mouth
of a bear. In the dark, we imagine its teeth. We do not sleep.
We have waking dreams, remember our sisters / mothers / aunties
picking berries in summer, how the juices stained darker
than engine oil. We stand slumped. We long for the softness of beds
but when we arrive and they help / push us out into the night,
we are in a nameless town and we are taken to rooms
with only a bed and sink. No window. Then we learn to despise beds
and miss the steady thrum of the engine. A lone cat / dog / bitch
is wailing outside, until someone feeds / kicks it. We wonder
who will come to rescue us. We hear the voices of men / men / men.

The Mother: *One day, a stone hit my windowpane, a sharp, insistent rap. I startled, turned. My daughter's haunted face peered back at me, framed by shadow. I flung the door open and wrapped her in the blanket of my body. She was breathless as she explained. She'd begged the Bear to let her out, let her visit us for just one day. And he was moved by her homesickness, how fierce it made her. He had let her come to us, as long as she promised not to speak with me alone. Her eyes darted to the door then, she bit her lip. Of course, she told me everything. Daughter, I said, this White Bear is a shifty one, a changeling. He must really be a troll. I gave her three yellow candles, told her to light them at night when he was asleep to see what was sharing her bed. Too soon she was gone. I stood holding her absence. On her first night back, she lit the candles as I told her to, gripping the match with a shaking hand and – there – his true form. He was a handsome prince. I wish I could have seen her face.*

The Handsome Prince

I am always locked inside the ottoman
of someone else's chest, or stored in the fridge
of the old man's heart. You cannot see me,
waving from behind the ogre's eyes
or breathing through the nostrils
of the lumbering troll. I am buried
deep as anger. I might be hidden
in the small, ridged body of a toad.
You look for me in every wishing well
and open mouth, every crevasse
and pothole, as if I could climb up to you.
You imagine my sand-blasted hair,
beach-warm skin, the smell of me,
sandalwood and sunlight on bookshelves.
You stare at the clouded face
of the man whose scent is whisky
and sweat and you try to kiss me out
as if I will land on your tongue
like an ice cube, then turn into water,
into silk, into skin, into myself,
tall and proud and capable.
But when you draw away,
his eyes are empty, your mouth
is dry and I am watching
from the bunched quickness
of a spider's shape, trying to reach you
trying to lower down a silver thread.

The Mother: *Even from afar, I sensed my girl was in trouble. She had broken the rules, woken her Prince by dropping tallow from the candle on his shirt. He told her that if she had held out a year, he would have been free, but now he was bound to go to his wicked stepmother (aren't they always) who had put a spell on him, enchanted him into this bear-shape. She lived in a castle East of the Sun and West of the Moon, and she'd schemed for him to marry her hideous daughter (aren't they always), a troll princess with a long nose. He vanished, and my daughter was alone, bereft again, searching for him. But I raised her strong. She knew what to do. She spoke to the sky, for the sky sees everything. She asked the East Wind to carry her, and it took her to the West Wind. The West Wind passed her to the South Wind. The South Wind passed her to the North Wind. She was handed around like a parcel. The North Wind said that he once blew an aspen leaf to the castle of the wicked stepmother and was exhausted after, but he would take her if she insisted. She's my daughter, she always insists.*

The North Wind

I know what it is to carry someone
to the unmapped place where aspen leaves
are blown. Do not tell me what weight is
unless you have lifted something
not with your shoulders, your body
but with the running stream of you,
the shifting heart of you, the restless
core of you. When I raised the girl high
she kept her arms clamped to her sides
like a shut parasol. I buoyed her up:
her armpits and her dress, the chapped soles
of her feet, her hair, her eyelashes and cuticles,
the pupils of her moss-coloured eyes.
I hoisted her to bird-height, sun-height,
the clouds became an afterthought.
I kept moving, afraid of dropping her,
afraid of her plummeting to the ground
and soon, I forgot myself in the ebb
and surge of effort. I saw the two of us
as a passing crow might: an absence,
a blue gown suspended in the sky
like a handkerchief dropped from a window
trying to glide to earth.

The Mother: *She arrived, lashed by weather. The castle was forbidding, her prince locked deep within its heart. She had to climb the walls, slip through doorways, become one with the night. She crept into the satin-draped room of the troll princess, woke her up and begged her, bargained to see the prince. But women stick together. It wasn't as tough as you'd think.*

The Princess With The Long Nose

If it were left to me, I'd only be betrothed
to mulberry Dior handbags, kiss-proof lipstick,
mascara so waterproof you could scuba-dive in it.
What good is a husband if no one
sees you wearing them? I want to be adorned
with gold drop earrings, pink hoodies
shouting the names of cities I've never visited.
I want a different shade for every season,
my cheeks like sunset, my eyelids latte brown.
I want to announce my long legs, the weir
of my hair and yes – my nose – Roman
and regal, stretching elegantly, cat-like
in the centre of my face. Let no one tell you
this is not what beauty is. I am my own make-up
artist. I only want a husband if he's pleated
and translucent, something to drape
ghostly on the back of my oak chair.

The Mother: *I often think about her empty heart. Ugly girls are someone's wife. I think about her and cast the spell. I'd like to sit she felt.*

she wants, buy whatever she likes.

the princess with her shopping basket full, scripted from the start. She can dress up how You're doomed in fairy tales unless you're mother too, the one who hatched the plan down with her, hear her stories, know what

The Step Mum

Wicked in nylons and a polka dot wiggle dress,
Cruella de Vil, mutton dressed as lamb.
Wicked cooking lasagne for someone else's child.
Wicked dancing on tables and drinking rosé.
Wicked folding a hundred pairs of pants,
tidying up the graveyard of odd socks.
Wicked as Bette Davis with a cigarette
dropping tiny stars of ash on the carpet.
Wicked doing the school run on Thursdays.
Wicked with envy, wicked *who is the fairest
of them all.* Wicked *look what happens when we
leave dad without child supervision.*
Wicked helping with homework.
Wicked *don't tell me what to do you're not
my mum.* Wicked weeping at bedtime.
Wicked turning the step-kids into toads
and cats. Wicked boiling them in soup
and serving them to their father, crusty ciabatta
on the side. Wicked called by the ex's name again.
Wicked pictures of their mum,
high cheekbones, perfected hair. Wicked
all that happiness immortalised. Wicked drinking
gin and smoking out of the bedroom window.
Wicked exiled to the castle of the troll.
Wicked beheaded at the wedding, just in time
still holding a bouquet of freesias,
a spot of blood staining
the chief bridesmaid's dress.

A Bluebeard Among The Blue Birds

Joelle Taylor

Beside her the digital screens winked like uncles:
a holiday a car a house a job a college
a spa new teeth new breath new air new—

and then, as one, the screens flickered, blanked

and the face of a man appeared
filling the line of screens
along the conveyor belt
around the curve and
on into the horizon.

BLUEBEARD! the sign
showed its teeth, grinned.

Martha and her shadow stopped, staring up at the vast billboard.
They wrapped their arms around each other.
Martha's mouth hung open, an unguarded gate.

#followthebeard the sign ordered
& Martha felt in her pocket for her phone.

Bluebeard was famous in Austerity.
An internet celebrity, a digital Jesus
a cyber prophet with a beard of constellations,
a leather jacket and sunglasses,
a matt black Harley Davidson
that ate the road it rode upon;
and Martha knew,

though he had a questionable reputation
and had been married six times &
though his alabaster face was cut and paste,
he was the
perfect
idea of Man, the ultimate in masculinity.

An insta-influencer, social media mogul
Bluebeard had 3-million followers across social media platforms
a new video a day, a new slither of advice.

> His skin was filtered smooth through a top cosmetic
> physician, & though
> some gossip journals wondered how many faces he had
> collected before finding this one,
> how many others he had hanging in his wardrobe;

Martha and her shadow stared in wonder.

> How like a conveyor belt was his smile,
> she thought,
> how like a journey;
> I wonder where it might take me.

The camera zoomed in on the centre of his eye
and in it she thought she saw
a small girl waving.

The sun was a stubbed cigarette
that barely lit the dimly streets;
silhouettes of families
glimpsed through grey gingham curtains
picked at the bones of birds;
a union jack fluttered
but could not find its wings

& a song escaped its leash.

Martha pushed her key into the lock
and stepped home at last
a tidy flat in a tower block
in the town at the edge of the world,
whose rooms were clean and sparse
with beds as tight as lips
and floors knuckle bright.

The whole flat silent
as though holding its breath.

She shared a room with her two elder sisters;
one at university, the other on night shift.
Martha's father was an empty chair,
an unsigned card, a space.
Though he died long ago he still lived in her face
the presence of absence;
she saw him sometimes
looking out from her eyes in the mirror
& though her mother did everything
in her power to be both,
Martha could not help but miss her father.

Loneliness is a thin dog that cannot find its tail.

Her mother was a nurse by day
& a cleaner by nightfall.
When Martha was small
she whispered that she polished the stars
so hard that they became windows
and if Martha stood on tip toes
pressed her nose against the panes
she could see her father again.

She brought her daughters up to stand as one
with their backs pressed against the wall,
but everyone was too busy for metaphors
hunting money to feed one penny at a time to their home
that Martha had to let herself in after school
and often ate alone.

Martha and her mother
sometimes shopped at the local food bank,
shuffling in line for hours
quietly showing their passports, mumbling apologetic thanks;
life was hard in Austerity as a single parent.

Martha threw her bag down
excited to get online and
#followthebeard.
Posters of Bluebeard and #HisWives
lined the walls over her bed.

It is possible to hold the whole world in one palm;
Martha logged in to the Bluebeard chatroom.

She had set up a fake profile using her mother's old mobile
posting a cartoon avatar instead of a real picture
and she found there were many girls like her online
pacing digital streets like electronic ghosts
hanging out on virtual corners
leaning heavily against posts.

They welcomed her, a lost sister, another one like them
all of them avatars
impersonations of themselves
leaving their shadows sat at school desks
older online, more independent
erudite and adventurous, more mischievous and curious
a girl-gang stalking cyber streets
unaware of any danger;
perhaps someone should have warned them:

never accept tweets from a stranger.

(III)

She clicked on
a flashing #FollowTheBeard

      And there he was, that smile, a light breeze dancing quiet.

Bluebeard strived for physical perfection, would spend hours in the gym
filming himself working out before uploading, & inviting
girls to share photos of themselves,
offering advice,
top tips #getinvolved.
Martha leaned forward;
he had the cosmos in his beard, sparkling as though it was Indra's web.

If only she had wondered
if other girls had been caught in there

just as they were in his bed.

The days passed like next door neighbours & social workers
& Martha counted her teeth,
her pockets as empty as baby birds' mouths,
her heart an abandoned playground.
Then one night just before bed
as she was pulling on threads in the web
weaving new worlds
#FollowTheBeard flaunted gaudily across the screen.
She clicked.

CONGRATULATIONS!!
BLUEBEARD IS TO MARRY!
THE QUESTION IS
TO WHO?
COULD IT BE YOU?

If you think you could be Bluebeard's newest wife
then post your bio to his profile.

Martha was a small girl staring face-on into the sun.

The other girls were suspicious
said that he was a
Bluebeard sat among the blue birds,
a cat in an aviary
who waited for girls to tweet their love, encouraged jealousy, then
waited for war to erupt. They said that Bluebeard did not care
that other people's suffering to him only equated to likes and shares;
and did she not remember the story of his missing wives?
It seemed the more Bluebeard misbehaved the more he was forgiven
they said
it seemed the more that he took the more that he was given.

Hashtag Bluebeard
Hashtag wherearehiswives?
Hashtag whereismydaughter?
Hashtag didtheyescapewiththeirlives?

They thought of him as a crime scene
but Martha saw him as a tunnel
she could escape through.

Bluebeard said the things
her lips drew back from.

If her shadow had a face it was his.

A thousand, thousand young women
answered the advertisement,
few able to resist the hypnotic electronic
metronomic enticement
dreaming they could leave their
municipal towers & tenements.

Come to Bluebeard, Bluebeard will give you a home.
Come to Bluebeard, you will never be alone.

So, Martha messaged him a greyscale photo &
told him about her greyscale life, and how it was
to live at the edge of the greyscale world &
she told him about her father, & how she still spoke to him in secret &
how grief is a heavy coat; she told him how
no one
understood her, & how Bluebeard was like a beacon to
girls like her.
She pressed send, then slipped soft to bed

unaware of the ripples stretching out across the web.

(V)

Bluebeard balanced long-legged in the centre of the web
unravelling threads, commenting & baiting
reeling in followers
spooling the internet from invisible spinnerets,

waiting.

(VI)

While she slept
blue birds circled her bed
& left notes in the shallow air.

The email was there when she awoke
a grinning thing, an extrovert
in orange & flash, it shouted:

CONGRATULATIONS!

& slowly Martha realised –
her stomach an elevator in a disaster film –
that she had won Bluebeard's hand
the man who she spoke to every night
had answered back.

In shock, Martha called her sisters
& they huddled around the phone
each of their faces hung like washing
as they read the email aloud.
Her mother watched from the door.

You are so lucky! her sisters sagely agreed
& Martha felt a flush of pride
that she had finally been seen, that
she belonged;
her spine grew three inches.

Just then the doorbell sang, and a parcel was left on the step
and inside lay a wedding dress, with a note from her husband-to-be
pinned to its breast:
Darling, wear this for me
and at the side was a small box marked 'engagement present'.

Inside
small jewelled hands mounted
on a platinum necklace
that met around her throat.
This is to remind you that you are in safe hands
read the accompanying letter, in delicate calligraphy
nooses and knots.
Her sisters fastened it, & Martha
gazed at her reflection, a girl trapped beneath ice.
It was an expensive gesture,
though her mother privately thought
the hands looked like they wanted to strangle

rather than offer her protection.

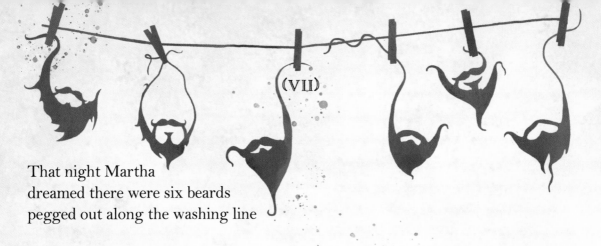

(VII)

That night Martha
dreamed there were six beards
pegged out along the washing line

The first sang *run*
The second sang *beware*
The third sang *be careful*
Of the man with the cold blue hair

The fourth sang *hide*
The fifth sang *say your prayers*
The sixth sang *be careful*
Of the man with the cold blue hair

(VIII)

After a sleepless night, Martha Thinbone's eyes were
round as wedding rings,
her heart a tolling church bell.
It did not feel like the best day of her life
more like a funeral. *Don't be silly*!
sang her sisters
It's a limousine not a hearse!
Her mother was about to speak
but her lips snapped shut like a purse.

Think of the money! chirruped her sisters
The fame! The prestige!

We will never be cold and hungry again!
We will have everything we need!

Their faces were open windows,
she could see what the marriage meant to them all.
Martha shook off her dream
as though it were a skinny dog
that had followed her home from school.

The dress lay supine, unmoving, with arms across its chest
interred in tissue paper. It looked like it had been
laid to rest
but together they dug it out and
held it up against Martha
who stood still in the morning sunlight,
circled by her sisters' laughter.
The fabric was screen printed with Bluebeard's image
selfies culled from social media
laced with pearls like tiny infant teeth
white as the flag of surrender;
it had diamonds like fossilised tears
studding the bodice and sleeves.

She held it up against the light,
far too small, they murmured, *far too tight*.
But they pulled and they tugged,
and they squeezed;
binding her to her new life
keeping her breath in a Tupperware box for later;

Her mother said nothing,
watching Martha prepare for the wedding and feast
discussing who they would see there, who would see them;
her mother had a strange feeling,
a knowing, a kind of curse;

that her daughter was being prepared
to be the main course.

(IX)

As a farewell gift, her mother fastened a rose to her lapel
whispering,

It's a very long, sharp pin
you must be careful with it, daughter
it's more dangerous than you can imagine.
Why, one tight thrust to the heart
or through a pulsing vein
and that would be the end of that,
blood falling like summer rain…

Startled, Martha clutched the pin
while her sisters opened their make-up kits.
They painted, sculpted, and erased her skin
until they found a face that fit her.
Martha did not recognise the woman in the mirror
entombed in the gilded frame.
She looked like someone she once knew

but could not remember the name.

(X)

Thousands lined the streets
or hung Bluebeard's picture from their flat windows
looking down on their hero
and the young woman far below.

Though butterflies comprised her living veil
& her bridal train was carried in the beaks of swallows
she did not feel special.

Martha was nervous and anxious
marching solemnly to the wedding service & banquet,
tight mouthed and trapped in her wedding dress
that seemed to wear her
& propel her forward;

lakes of sweat pooling at the nape of her neck
but she knew she must be grateful, she was chosen
and the world would soon be very different.

Bluebeard stood before her with an appraising expression
as though he were a farmer at market, testing cattle.
She stood shyly and let his eyes weigh her
before being guided gently toward the chapel.

Somehow somewhere
her mother lost her grip of her hand
as Martha was swept into the ceremony

& lasers slashed the air in bold stripes of crimson
& petals eddied around them in a soft white monsoon.

The ceremony was attended by social media stars, insta-influencers
YouTube celebrities, and names she could not remember;
each of the seats filled with luminaries, the thin and the famous
with a start, she realised the whole congregation
was formed of strangers.
Bluebeard, where is my family? Martha asked quietly
as her mother waved weakly from the back of the crowds
her sisters shouted something, but the room was too loud.
Bluebeard turned to her

Darling it's streamed around the world, they may as well watch from home.

***

The room silenced and vows were whispered;
confetti erupted across the crowd like a great white blizzard
that settled in drifts across the couple.
The wedding ring reverently offered was a snow globe
containing the town at the edge of the world
its tiny streets flickered with lights
reflected softly in the eyes of the girl

and for a moment everything was still
and everything was perfect

everything was beautiful and she knew
the marriage would be worth it.

***

At the banquet, there in the centre of the table,
a pig lay, legs outstretched
its mouth stuffed with an apple
it's eyes pomegranates
the invited diners chuckled and roared
pulling off pieces of its flesh
as Martha stared in dawning disbelief
at her untamed wedding guests. Then
Bluebeard stood, wiping his beard and chin
on a hand-pressed rose damask linen napkin
proposing a toast to the gathered reception.
Thank you all, he preened, *for attending my wedding*
quite forgetting his bride,
who straightened the edges of her smile
& raised her wine glass
watching his beard dancing in the reflection.

She'd had too much to drink, too much fun, but
in the wine's mirror she thought she saw
the beard snake out from his face, & launch
across the table toward the pig;
the whiskers sniffing the air like a livid dog, until
it found the beast, paused, then rose up, a tsunami,
its shadow engulfing the animal
before pouncing & biting
snapping back to its master with the meat
who stroked it tenderly,
placing the morsel softly
on the tip of his long blue tongue.

The whole congregation whooped and cheered
Hip hip hooray, they bellowed, *raise your glass to Bluebeard!*

Martha Thinbone placed her wine glass back on the table
& reached toward the water.

(XI)

Night fell like black rain across Austerity.

Finally, it was time to say goodbye to their guests
who slowly picked up their coats, promised to text, and left
leaving husband and bride
stood at the door to the rest of their lives.

Bluebeard pulled out a heavy silver key
ornate and inlaid with filigree, & as they both turned
toward their living quarters' door
Martha's small heart stuttered and soared, all
doubts autumn leaves beneath her feet.

She held the hand of her husband with his thick red-carpet smile
and knew she was crossing a threshold between woman and child.

Bluebeard grinned, slid the key into the lock
the door opened hesitantly

and Martha was lost.

(XII)

That night she dreamed
his beard was a dark waterfall
plummeting from his chin
& that debris was tangled up in it
& in the wild waters raging
she thought she saw her family
swept up in the flood, waving,
their hands slipping further away
& when she leaned closer
she saw the river was of blood,
her reflection caught in its
night currents.

(XIII)

The first day of the marriage
Martha felt a foreboding, a nagging unease
as though she had a small seed caught between her teeth –
at breakfast she ate little and sat
staring instead at his beard
considering all the things it reminded her of.

It was blue as a new bruise
or as sadness, or as grief.
As dark as an unfathomable sea,
with grey things living deep beneath;
a shark fin appearing on the skyline.

(XIV)

After they had eaten, Bluebeard,
his smile a thin paper cut,
held out before her a bouquet of keys.
My tower block is comprised of one hundred floors, he said
and on each of the floors are one hundred or more doors
and you can enter any of them
but one.

He took her on a safari around her new home;

this room is a nightclub, he said
revealing a spectrum of strobing lights,
she felt the deep vein of music
saw dancers slumped against the walls
that would awaken at the dawn of night.
The beard said nothing.

& this room, he shouted, *is October
1954*
a settee, a rug, a tin bath
even a draft excluder beneath the door
anti-macassars lined the backs of chairs
& a coal fire sang to the wireless
of Russia, America, the Cold War.
The beard said nothing.

With strange gravity he unlocked the next room
& Martha was blinded by a violent spotlight
Lights, camera, action, quiet please! he screamed
you can be the star of your own cinema
all you have to do is believe!
We can make our own films, Bluebeard purred, a hand upon her shoulder
Something that we can both look back on.
The beard said nothing.

& this room is the lost Library of Alexandria!
There were shelves from ceiling to floorboards
a thousand books with their backs turned
that would only open for Bluebeard
& sometimes when she passed by the room
in the deep pools of night
she thought she heard them gossiping
She won't last she won't last she won't–.

All day Bluebeard led her on the wild tour
until they finally stopped at an insignificant small grey door.
His voice lowered with intensity,
you must never enter this room, he whispered,
though I trust you with the key.
His eyes grew wild like boats lost at sea,
a snake slithered under his skin.

You can go anywhere at anytime
except for this one thing.
Never enter this room, child
or I swear there will be blood.
No one who enters this room
can ever leave, is that understood?

The keyhole looked like her mother's silhouette.

Daughter, she thought it warned,
mind your curiosity.

***

But wherever Martha went she thought about the key.
She thought about the door.
It followed her into her dreams
bone-muttering: *gentle Martha, open me.*
How heavy in your hand
is the small gold key?

(XV)

That night she dreamed
that all the doors across the house
were whispering her name,
chattering as if they were mouths
and when she listened carefully
wrapped tightly in her bed
she thought she heard
the forbidden room mourn:

All gone! All dead!

She knew he carefully watched
over her & web cameras were hidden
all over the tower; she saw them winking
their red eyes at one another,
even in her bedroom or in the shower, and she could not help
but wonder if the red eyes all knew each other.

But as her husband watched her, she watched him,
carefully appraising when he was not looking.

She could not help but notice sometimes
that the beard seemed to be breathing
as though it could escape his face while he was sleeping
and roam the streets, grieving and searching
for something lost.
And once she thought she saw her husband hand-feeding his beard
crooning *settle down darling.*
& often, she dreamed he hunted
wild beards with nets
catching them by their hundreds and keeping
them all as domestic pets.
She wondered if perhaps that was what she heard
calling from the forbidden room.

Was the beard the puppet or the master?

She kept her thoughts close and quiet;
Bluebeard had a temper
though he kept it fenced behind white teeth.
Sometimes when he smiled
it looked like he was eating raw meat
& Martha learned quickly to read his somersaulting moods
though there was something about her
that always seemed to make him angry
no matter what she did, something small and hidden.
He was a hurricane in a living room
& she a young tree
bending.

Strangely for an internet star
Bluebeard's tower was off-grid
her phone would not work and
none of the computers were connected; he needed
some privacy
life was not easy, he said, *living as a web celebrity*

and so, boredom became her best friend
spending hours together.
The lack of WiFi
distanced
her from her family and friends;
marriage to this man was lonely and isolating;
missing those hurried mornings with her mother
throwing stories across the table like cards,
those late nights with the girls
skimming pebbles across digital lakes.
Once, she had held her own fluttering heart in her hands
& held it up to the wind

now she held her phone high instead
staring at the bars
as though they were a rainbow
she must reach the end of.
She climbed the stairs
& as she neared the top landing
she passed the forbidden door
it twitched as she walked past
but held its tongue
and she walked on, & up & up
until she reached the roof
& her phone awarded her reception.
Quickly she sat down
and, fumbling, found a connection.

Her cyber-sisters were ecstatic
to see she was online
they thought they had lost her forever.

She sat there for hours chattering
not noticing the time; and
telling them about the thousand rooms,
the keys, and the forbidden door
and the drudgy dreary boredom
of life as Bluebeard's latest like;
and the fear. The quiet crouching fear,
an animal that lived beneath their beds.

But then the front door moaned
and Bluebeard was home
slamming the breath out of life.

His shadow waited outside;

even it wanted to avoid him.

***

That night at dinner, Bluebeard,
his grin a guillotine,
questioned her about her new life:
was she happy? did she miss her friends?
did she love him? did she love him? did she–
Martha, her eyes unlit rooms
her hands knotted
counted the ways.
He liked her to keep her tongue;
girls should be quiet, he often said,
especially when they are speaking.

Well, he quietly announced
you will be on your own for a while;
business is taking me away.

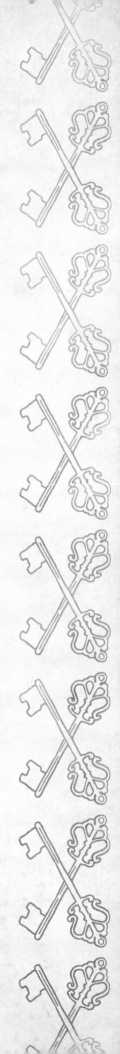

You can do what you want and be who you want to be,
you can play in any room at all, but never use the golden key.
There are simply some things that women
are not meant to see.
Never ever ever use the golden key.

(XVIII)

The dark came to the town like a stray dog.
Lights went out as though blown,
& the people of Austerity huddled together far below.

Something is coming, something is already here.
The townspeople scanned the skies in trepidation
and fear
before turning as one to stare at the blackened tower block
of Bluebeard.

(XIV)

As soon as he left, Martha headed back to her rooftop sanctuary
shaking off tension like a tight dress
& pausing for a moment, stroking the small gold key
as she passed the door to the forbidden room.
& though she tried hard she could not resist
the squeal of the key squirming in the tight of her fist
as it sang,
girls are inquisitive, and girls are explorers
girls push their noses into the darkest of corners.

She had to know more about this man she had married.

She slid the key into the lock and opened the door

and behind it:

a room with blank walls and bare wooden floor;
and in the centre a laptop, open on a desk.
She walked toward it slowly, &
as she neared, the golden key blinked red
& a small metal tongue cleanly
emerged from its tip.

A key turned in Martha's head.

She had not only unlocked the door
but the whole mystery:
the key was not a key but a USB.

She clicked the key into the computer
and the screen jumped to a strange website
a live feed to a dimming living room,
figures almost visible in the twilight.
It took a moment to process what she was seeing.

Some dungeons are digital.
Some vaults are virtual.

A gallery of girls caught on the web like flies;
a gallery of girls who believed a handsome man's lies,
hanging like paintings across the virtual walls
or like carcasses in a butcher shop display.

Slowly, Martha backed away, a retreating tide.

Oh, the blood and pain and the horror!
Oh, the grief and the loss and the torture!
The betrayal of trust, the dishonour!

Her eyes were drawn back to the young women
each one of them somehow invisible, a watermark on air.

But was that not Ayo from the year above her own?
Who went missing after volleyball,
whose mother is a shadow in a window &
father made a prospector
who sifts the streets for his child?

And surely that is Joanne?
An easy girl to ignore
with translucent skin
a face like a screwed poem.
She was never more popular
than when she had gone missing,
now everyone in Austerity was her friend.

And no, that can't be Kim-Ye? The girl from college
always in detention, always late, always 'always'
a little too much.
The kind of girl who gives each of her knuckles
names & waits for boys
after school, notches like grave markers on her belt;
her fists bouquets hanging at her side.

She did not know the other girls
but all his missing wives were there;

red dresses on a rail.

Martha backed away from the screen
her scream was a ghost that haunted the house
& ran through the town below.

Shopkeepers stopped with tills gaping.
Birds flew backwards.

The girls' faces were looted shop windows
bruised fruit, abandoned streets;
she shouldn't be so surprised from a man who would
Instagram the apocalypse,

Beneath the live feed was a caption
Welcome, it read
to Bluebeard's Personal Online Dungeon.

She slammed the laptop lid
wrenching out the USB,
her skin dancing just above her bones
her teeth a crescendo.
She had to get a message to the families & police,
the social media star was
a murderer and a thief.

He stole girls from poor families
he kept their hearts in a jar,

he placed the jar in the darkest cupboard
where they sparkled like stars

and slowly the stars dimmed
and wounds healed and scarred

and slowly we forgot their names
no obituary, memorial, memoir.

(XX)

She felt the room thicken
and a darkness crawl in as though it were living.

Bluebeard had returned without warning,
bringing the silence with him.

When he finally spoke, it was a summer storm.
The ground shivered & the walls closed their eyes,
tongues of lightening flickered across his beard
his heart a hurricane
and Martha knew that she
would be hung in his
gallery of girls
an exhibit, a still-life, fine art.

You traitor!
You Judas!
Why are females all so curious?
You traitor!
You Judas!
Why are females all so curious?

His beard played shadow puppets on the wall:
she saw it as a cliff, she saw herself fall.

        Then the shadow beard became a blade
        she saw herself impaled, she saw her own grave.

Now she saw it as a titanic blue wave
saw herself drowning, both arms raised
helpless on the surging tide of his rage.

        His heart was a black hole dragging everything in
        his soul a swinging light in an empty building.

His laugh was Armageddon
each of his hands, apocalypse.

She pleaded softly with him
but his eyes were a total eclipse.

His lips were a fault line seconds before a natural disaster.

*Now you are another girl that will need to be sacrificed
you can take your position next to my former wives.*

Martha trembled before him, angry at her own fear.
Please just a few minutes, she pleaded, *just to say my prayers.*

He stopped and smiled like a slit throat

*You can have seven and half minutes in full.
Say your prayers then return to me*

her running feet ticked into the distance.

***

Martha headed for the roof;
she had to get a message out there
people had to know the truth, about—

*Three thousand steps
three thousand steps
Martha climbed the tower
in just one breath.*

the lies & the violence & the isolation & fear
people should know about
the pretty monster called Bluebeard.

Three thousand steps
three thousand steps
Martha scaled the tower
in just one breath.

She held her phone up to get reception.

Three thousand steps
three thousand steps
Bluebeard's running up the stairs
in just one breath.

Connecting,
fingers thick as horses' hooves,
she posted and messaged
sent files, & photographs
each message reading like an epitaph:

#Bluebeardiscoming
#Bluebeardisonthestair
#Bluebeardisatthedoornow
#Bluebeardhearmyprayer

(XXI)

He stood at the top of the stair, a smile lassoing his lips
appraising the young woman whose body did not quite fit.

She dropped the phone and dropped her head,
insignificant in his shadow, already dead.

Oh, my heart!
Oh, my blood!
I swear that I am sorry,
I swear on the sisterhood.

His beard was a loom of entrails like in the myth of the Furies,
Erinyes, each strand of hair a lifeline severed; &
was that his wives she saw hanging
from its dark branches?

The engagement necklace tightened around her throat
its hands meeting in violet prayer, as Bluebeard leaned in,
all glitter and glory;
But as she slipped from the skin of the world
the ghost of her remembered mother,
returned insisting: the rose! The rose!
The rose and the pin!

She lashed out at him with it;
Bluebeard buckled and hissed
his beard a wild cat.
She could not believe this aberration
was the same man she had kissed
whose posters had been a father.

She ran and was almost at the staircase
when Bluebeard's blue beard leapt savagely
from his face, a growl caught in its teeth,
tendrils of hair worming from it
and holding her firmly to the ground
as Bluebeard strode over sneering, a
giggle of blood studding his lips

Martha posted a final prayer
to all the young women like her, who
thought they were invincible in love,
or walked digital streets alone,
or searched for a replacement father
in the darkest of corners.
Now she understood
how a stranger's kiss can kill
and marriage vows lead to murder

& her final thoughts were for her sisters,
her beautiful broken mother
her kintsugi smile.

Then,
thick shadows around the roof burst into blue birds
that screamed across the skies, their bitter song a curse.

Bidh nigheanan ag èisteachd.

Damn you Bluebeard
may your beard become a noose.
Damn you Bluebeard
the world will know the truth.

Bidh nigheanan ag èisteachd.

With the last note of the song Bluebeard's eyes,
once boiling cauldrons of rage,

stuttered, dimmed and lost their light.

     Blood scattered across the rooftop like red confetti,
     like seeds.
     The sky stood still & hung its head.
     Birds lined the iron railings,
     mourners at a funeral.

Bluebeard's face emptied and he crashed to the floor

and behind him,
her elder sisters both real and virtual:
one with a shaking machete in fist

all of their faces, war.

(XXII)

Here lies the true story of Bluebeard
and of men like him across the world,

        who haunt digital corridors with nets and nasty threats
        to catch young girls.

Most folk tales are lessons so here is this one's moral:
the question is not if this is a tale of curiosity
and betrayal

        or even a question of marriage or of murder.
        The real question is, did Martha open the door,

or did the door open Martha?

NYAMINYAMI

Kayo Chingonyi

nyaminyami

in a country named for its river, where the river is wide and its flow gives life to those who live on its banks, in a valley where the people and the river lived in accord for generations, woven as hair in a braid is woven, in such a place our story begins, half a lifetime ago before the Monkton Comission when people burned their chitupas in front of the offices of district commissioners, before a blood condition passed through the population as flame passes through a forest, before load shedding, hours of powercuts; the national grid sold off to the highest bidder, before the country was booming from copper and the roads were full of American cars and the salesmen plied their trade with sweet nothings, weaving through the traffic to make their entreaties: my friend you must hurry up and catch this Mustang before it gallops away. Before pot holes and roads unfinished through lack of investment, before imported knock offs, before the goods trains and trucks, before the valley was connected by the orderly topography of macadam and the valley's foot-worn pathways, taught to the valley's young by experience, were paved. The valley people lived in a relative peace. Livingstone was, by then, long dead and the people were free to bide after their own fashion, giving honour to the god of the river and, in return for their supplication, receiving blessings in the form of fish which were so plentiful that to a child who did not like fish a parent would say my darling, here there is fish or there is fish and the child would remember the legacy knitted in to the songs they had known all their lives of fisherfolk who swam before they could walk or talk because the river god would never let them sink

… the river god

like many gods is a vengeful god   but who would not
want vengeance   separated from   their lover
by the insistence of machinery   the promise of copper
the future   open   to those brave enough to take it
always this human mania for taking   the river god
remembers   what is forgotten   between generations
slavers raided   in the name   of this selfsame progress
and who was it   through all of this   who   provided
no man   nothing so inflexible as that   but this god
part serpent   though don't believe what they tell you
about serpents   part fish   able to swim   and be one
with water   holding water   in a flowing order
no man-made machine   could conjure   though the strangers
who came with their ideas   of order   their instruments
and blueprints   those strangers brought with them a plan
to build a dam   harness the river's power to bolster
the power of man   and what did it matter to them
dishonouring a god   in whom they didn't believe

for those who believed   the dam   was no boon
they knew   no human hand could bend the landscape
to the ends of capital   without consequence
and so they offered prayers and bade their kinfolk
agree to nothing   sign nothing   refuse the handshakes
that   to these strangers   constitute contracts
and though believers feared the river god's wrath
the dam was built   the strangers executed their plan
and what did it matter that the skies brought forth
unprecedented rain a mere trifle   and those swept away
were unlucky but what had that to do with the dam
which would bring about such prosperity in this land
believers knew   the waters raged   in the river god's name
that in the quest for progress   we often make mistakes
make beds   in which our descendants sleep badly
in our haste to acquire to own to feed
a monster which cannot be sated   for all you fill
with minerals its   waiting   capacious   mouth

'water can crash and water can flow'

who gave them   licence   to live here
who brought them   succour   refuge
what gave them   the right
to come between   this centuries-old   love
what do they know   of love
who have not loved outside   human time
this wall they built in all their wisdom
can only delay   our reunion
those   who know water   know
eventually water will pass through
even   the smallest gap   in what appears
to the human eye   to be   a solid mass

epilogue

it is said that after the concrete
after the rain
after the valley
shifted from its old ways
all that remained
of nyaminyami
was a small statue
marking the place

a fish-headed snake
a caption
consigning the river god
to the realm of legend
as if all this water
flowed here by some accident
as if the old ways
were only stories

but to this day pilgrims
sometimes see a momentary swell
in the course of the river
and those who recognise these eddies
know this to be nyaminyami testing
the limits of human ingenuity
calling out to a lover who is constant
as the motion of water

Moon Station 5

Will Harris

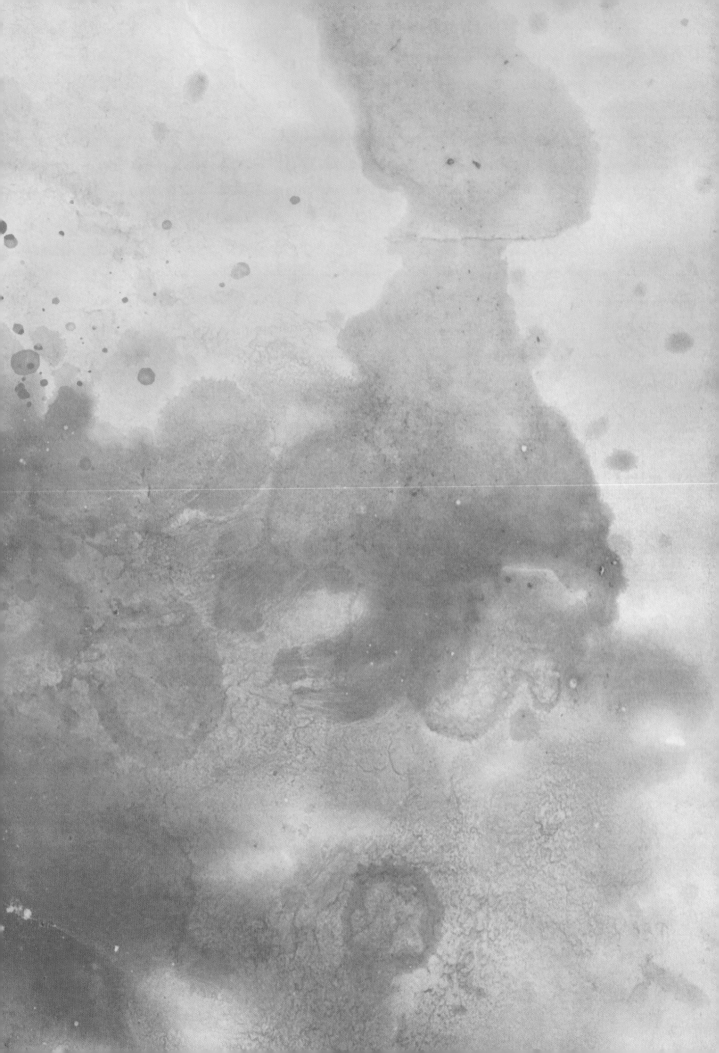

MOON STATION 5

Will Harris

The story you're about to read is a a version of a version of a version. A song covered so many times no one can remember how the original goes.

It re-versions the ancient story of the Greek warrior Philoctetes, most famous for two things: his magical bow and his foot wound, which smelt horrendous.

Philoctetes first appears on the outer fringes of Homer's *Iliad*. The *Iliad* was written down almost 3,000 years ago, but passed around long before that beside campfires and at festivals. Homer recounts the final phase of the ten-year siege of Troy by the Greek army, a bloody struggle that saw the Greeks emerge victorious, spearheaded by heroes like Achilles, Ajax, Odysseus and the lesser-known Philoctetes.

An epic like the *Iliad* requires an epic cast of characters, in part because so many of them are killed off. Philoctetes is like Bucky Barnes's Winter Soldier in *Avengers: Endgame*. He may only appear glancingly in the final cut, but we know his story extends far beyond it.

In 409 BC, the writer Sophocles decided to honour Philoctetes by making him the hero of his own story. The play he wrote focuses on his time marooned on the holy island of Lemnos.

But first, some background: Philoctetes had been sailing with other warriors, including Odysseus, to join the Greek army in the fight against Troy. Stopping at Lemnos to pay their respects, Philoctetes was bitten on the foot by a snake and the resulting wound failed to heal. It became so smelly, in fact, that Odysseus and the others chose to abandon him and set sail to Troy by themselves.

The other main piece of background is the aforementioned magical bow. Hercules was the bow's original owner, but after mistakenly putting on a poisoned shirt he was in constant agony. His only way out was death. Everyone was too scared to light his funeral pyre, except for his friend Philoctetes – this was before the trip to Lemnos. In return for setting him ablaze, Hercules gave Philoctetes his bow, one that never missed its target.

Which takes us to Lemnos. With war raging elsewhere, Philcotetes is a bitter man, abandoned and nursing a smelly wound, in possession of a magical bow that won't do him much good now. In Sophocles's play, there are two other characters who arrive on the island: Odysseus (again) and Neoptolemus, son of great Achilles. Odysseus – wily, war-hardened – has been informed that Philoctetes's bow will be crucial to ending the Trojan War, so he brings along Neoptolemus – young, gullible – to help him obtain it at any cost.

The story you're about to read takes many liberties with the old myths. For one thing, it's set not in the distant past but the far future: on a training camp for soldiers called Moon Station 5. I've also extended the cast of characters and made Philoctetes the son of Hercules, rather than his friend. I did this to sharpen the similarities between him and Neoptolemus (called Toll in my story). Both live in the shadow of more famous heroes. Both are struggling under burdens: the weight of expectation, the shame of a wound. How will they define who they are for themselves?

Most of the best stories are derivative – they draw from other stories. This gives a lot of freedom to authors, and to readers too. You can always make the story your own in the retelling.

Interviewer: *Thank you for agreeing to this interview, Leda. It would help if you could start by telling us when you first encountered him on Moon Station 5. Could you sense that he was different?*

Leda: I heard him first.

The sound of one foot
dragging on concrete,
one foot
slightly behind the other.

Like a wounded lion, that's
what I thought.

Like a lion being led back to the zoo. Except
he didn't look like a lion.

He looked kind of mangy. Just a boy.
I wasn't impressed.

He waded into our world of war. Of training
for war. He was wearing
a dirty tracksuit, his backpack clutched
to his chest, face hidden by a ridiculous beanie.

It was meant to be an honour training here.

The Instructor watched on.
Jewel kicked the ball to me. I passed it.
A tackle came in. Someone shanked it wide.
The cage rattled.
The rattle echoed through the warehouse.

Like the way you smell pizza
before the doorbell rings, they caught
his scent. Jewel was first to react.
What have we got here?

The Instructor watched on.

He did smell bad, the new boy.
Like sliced ham. Mouldy bread. Sweaty boxers.
Each bad smell hiding something worse.

He was scratching at his hand.

I thought of a lion again,
or of a small cat licking its injured paw.

Everyone lined up to rattle the cage.
Jewel howled. *He looks as rank as he smells.*
The others howled too.

He clutched his backpack to his chest
as he came past. Like it was the only thing
that kept him upright.

The Instructor watched on.

The cage rattled.
The rattle echoed through the warehouse.

But the mangy boy, he wasn't scared.

Interviewer: *Were you aware of the weapon at the time? That's what people want to know. When did you see the weapon?*

Leda: Not then. But there was something
different in him. Or he brought
difference with him.
The stars turned above us.

Interviewer: *Thank you for giving us your side of the story, Toll. As you know, Leda has been talking to us. Maybe you could start with your arrival on Moon Station 5 on Day 3703?*

Toll: I don't know why you'd call it that.

Interviewer: *Sorry. On the day of your arrival.*

Toll: I arrived with General Odysseus and we were taken to the Instructor's office. I wasn't impressed with the set-up. The Gym has a reputation for producing heroes but it was a dirty warehouse in the middle of nowhere. Like somewhere they'd turn horses into glue, not make heroes. The Instructor sat there. Odysseus talked and talked. I looked at the photos on the wall. One photo, in particular. I almost shouted out to Odysseus, but then I thought it must have been a mistake. Had to be.

Interviewer: *I'm sure we'll come to the photo later. Can you tell us when you met him?*

Toll: Philoctetes? That morning. We were sharing a cell. He wasn't too friendly – said to call him *Lock*, which made sense. *Who threw away the key?* I asked. He seemed shell-shocked without ever having seen a shell. Just lay in bed, fully clothed. The smell was worse than a shit silo. *Lock*, I said, *I hear you just got in? I arrived from Hellenos earlier. Sorry if I talk a lot.* And then I started talking about my dad. *I blame him for most things. He wasn't a talker. The opposite. I guess that's the point of having a "reputation". It speaks for you. "Achilles, oh yes. Let me arrange that. Your son won't miss you."* That got his attention.

Interviewer: *You told him your father was Achilles? Did he talk about his father?*

Toll: Not in so many words.

Interviewer: *So you didn't know what happened?*

Toll: Not in so many words. Something bad happened, that was obvious. But he kept circling around it.
He said he felt like a dumb dog following his dad's shadow.
Then he got angry when I took that the wrong way.
He said his dad was a hero. *Sure*, I said. *No question.*

The horn blew for Gym.

Interviewer: *So he didn't tell you his father was Hercules?*

Toll: Not in so many words.

DAY 3704

Interviewer: *Tell me about what happened the next day?*

Leda: It started out like most days. Sleeping quarters.
Mess hall. Locker room. Workout. And within five minutes

Jewel's knee was pressed into the back of some kid's neck.
The Instructor watched on. Jewel twisted his ear

until it was pink as bubblegum. About to burst.
Then the new boy appeared. Lock. Dressed the same.

There were jokes. Digs. *I thought they incinerated the trash.*
Another new boy appeared. Smiling, blond.

He said his name was Toll. The Instructor cleared his throat.
We have the honour of welcoming General Odysseus here.

He'll take charge of training. Odysseus swam into view,
chin like the prow of a cruise ship. A different creature.

He glowed under the strip-lights. You couldn't get a fix
on him.
And when he talked it was like nothing anyone had heard.

Talk so smooth he ate the words off your tongue.

> *My young friends,*
> *it's been ten years of war.*
> *Think of those battles, year on year…*
> *How many of you grew up on tales*
> *of lost parents, lost*
> *siblings, bodies tossed*
> *on scrapheaps. Gathered here*
> *you have the chance to tip the scales.*
> *I know you've heard the songs.*
> *"No One Is an Outcast*
> *Who Has Hope," "Every Advance*

Brings Glory to the Corps,"
"Every Battle Brings the Chance
to Right Past Wrongs."
But I believe them, friends.
Together we can make this year the last.

Interviewer: *General Odysseus has a reputation for talking his way out of dead ends.*

Leda: Every day we'd trained for war. I'd been there since I was thirteen. No parents. No choice. But I wanted to be called up.

To end the war. That's what we were training for. To leave behind the Gym's four walls. The Instructor never liked me though.

Speed – fine. Stamina – fine. Bow work – poor. And then Odysseus said he wanted to see our bow work. Shooting practice.

Interviewer: *What was the significance of the bows, if you don't mind me asking? No one fights with bows and arrows in a war.*

Leda: To shoot a phaser you press a button. To use a bow you have to become – it's hard to describe – like an extension of

the bow's soul. The tension in its string has to match your own. Too weak, it wanders. Too firm, it flops. The bow knows you.

Interview: *What did Odysseus want you to do that day?*

Leda: Targets dropped from the ceiling. Whoever failed to hit their target and retrieve their marker would be expelled.

The targets moved. They were shaped like Striven.
Enemy arms raised in terror.
The ground beneath us shook.

Where's your weapon? Odysseus said, turning to Lock.
Lock was silent. Simmering. I offered him my spare bow.

He took it. Lights dimmed. The horns blew.

Interviewer: *Go on.*

Leda: It's hard to say what happened. A lot. I focused
on my bow. Kept my posture. Hit my target. Dodged arrows.

Retrieved my marker pinned to the Striven's chest. It was then
I realised it was a real body. Face scrunched in pain.

General Odysseus smiled. Lock was standing stock-still.
He wasn't even trying. He raised his bow and pointed it at

the General. The horns blew again. *Time up.* The strip lights
came on. In the centre of the room lay Jewel. He'd been injured.

Caught in the crossfire. Lock went over to help him.
He took the marker from Jewel's target and gave it to him.

Odysseus smiled. *A noble gesture.* But Jewel was mad.
He was shouting. *I'd rather be thrown out than take his help.*

You know this trash is the son of Hercules? You know that?
And he killed him. This piece of trash killed Hercules.

Interviewer: *That must have been a shock to hear.*

Leda: It was. I mean, I guess it was. I was staring at Lock
the whole time. He didn't flinch. His eyes were like two arrows

aimed at Odysseus's throat. I couldn't understand why.
I felt the stars turn above us. Things were changing.

And there was no Instructor.
Odysseus was waiting by the treadmills.
He was acting differently.

Toll: I could tell that, too. He seemed almost desperate.

Leda: The varnish chipped away.

Toll: That morning, the session was running an hour late.

Leda: Lock hadn't arrived.

We had to start Gym together.
That was the rule.
On time, at the same time.

Toll: Odysseus hated children. He hated waiting.

For him, everyone was a means to an end.
And he was here for Lock. For Lock's weapon.
He was tired of waiting for it.

Leda: When Lock finally stumbled in
he looked worse than usual.
The beanie was off, exposing a sprawl
of greasy hair. There were jokes.
Half-hearted digs. People backed off.

Toll: But Odysseus came to life.
There would be a punishment. That's war.
Discipline and punishment.

Leda: Hands came out from behind me.
The Instructor. He held me like
a tin of sliced peaches.

Toll: Odysseus was telling Lock his punishment.
I wasn't sure he understood.

Leda: He could hardly look up. The light hurt him.

Toll: Seven more Striven people were being lowered
by chains from the warehouse rafters.
It was too far away to tell if they were alive.

Shoot the targets.
That was Odysseus's order.
Miss one target and Leda goes to Moon Station 9.

Everyone froze.

Leda: Lock was told to fetch his weapon.

Toll: I followed him to the lockers. He was crying.
I wasn't sure he understood.

I kept saying sorry sorry sorry.
He didn't know what I was apologising for.

I took the bow out of my locker.
He wasn't angry at me for taking it.
He was still shocked. I shoved it into his arms.

That was the first and last time I saw it in the light.

Polished elm, smooth as syrup. Carved
with the symbols of Hercules: a lion's paw
and nine-headed water beast. Steel-tipped
points. An ox-gut string that shone like a river.

It's not my weapon to wield, I said.

Life seemed to flow from the weapon
back into Lock. But he was wary.
I think he was afraid of its power,
of how it might change him.

I told him what Odysseus had told me.
The weapon was going to end the war.
We needed to obtain it at all costs.

But I didn't want to go through with it.
The plan didn't matter. It was Lock's weapon.
His destiny.

Leda: I saw them come back in. My arms hurt.
The Instructor watched on.

The bow in Lock's hand wasn't mine.
It looked like a long white bird
folded in on itself. Poised to strike.

Toll was holding something shiny. At first
I thought it was a knife but then it wobbled.
I hadn't seen a photo for years.

Toll: I didn't know what was going to happen.
Lock only told me what to say and when.

Leda: Odysseus smiled. He was himself again.
In control and talking.

He extended an arm, and as he did
I heard a tearing sound
in my left ear. High and clear.
A hole ripped in the air.

The Instructor's grip went. He fell backwards
with a thump. Rigid as a door.

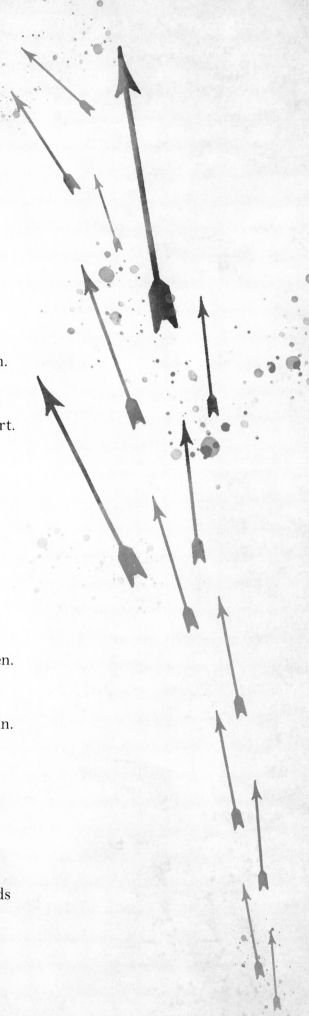

There was an arrow jammed in his left eye socket.
No blood. Sparks flew.

Toll: I held up the photo like Lock told me to.

I'd seen it in the Instructor's office the first day
we arrived, but not understood what it meant.
I thought it must have been a mistake
until Lock explained.

Day 10987, that's what this photo says.
We've been told a lie. Every day.

Today isn't Day 3705.
It's whatever they say it is.

I shouted loud enough that everyone could hear.

Ten years of war.
That's what we were told.

Lies.

Leda: Someone shouted about Lock killing Hercules.

How can we trust him?

Toll: Hercules chose death because he was in pain.
He hated Odysseus and the war.

He wasn't killed. Lock took mercy on him.
He lit his funeral pyre to give him a hero's death.

You want proof? I shouted. *Before he died,*
Hercules passed this bow to Lock.

He knew it would end the war,
just not how they imagined.

Leda: It would end the lie of the war.

Toll: The war hasn't been going on for years.
It's been decades. A never-ending war.

Leda: Lock shot the seven Striven down.

Toll: Odysseus was silent. Tongue-tied.

Interviewer: *He's since rediscovered his voice in the War Trials, of course. We eagerly await the verdict there. But I wonder if I could ask you the question I started with. Could you sense that Philoctetes was different?*

Leda: He was different because he was like us,
only he couldn't hide his wounds.
He carried his difference with him.

Toll: I think Hercules knew.

Interviewer: *About what?*

Leda: The wound and
the bow.

Toll: That's why the others made digs. Laughed.
They were ashamed. We all were.
We hid our shame behind our disgust.

To become a hero
you have to fear the bow
and love the wound.

Interviewer: *That's a nice phrase.*

Toll: It's what Lock said when I gave him back his bow.
The bow meant nothing without the wound.

Interviewer: *Do you have anything to add Leda?*

Leda: I keep thinking back to the night he arrived.

There were no windows
in the warehouse. It was a cavern
of steel walkways and strip lights.

The night Lock arrived,
dragging one foot behind the other
like a wounded lion,

I remember the lights reflected
against the wall made shapes
I'd never seen.

The moon over a field of grass,
swaying. A mother singing
from her windowsill.

It was there the whole time.
I just hadn't been looking
the right way.

THE MAKING OF A DWEN

Malika Booker

THE MAKING OF A DWEN

Malika Booker

The Dwen is a cautionary Caribbean folk tale which warns young children to beware of strangers, especially children, and is popular in countries like Trinidad and Grenada. It can be spelt Dwen (Grenada) or Douen or duenne (Trinidad)*. The Dwen is the spirit of a baby who died during childbirth or before they were christened and now resides in the land of limbo. The Dwen lures young children into deep forests where they either disappear never to be seen again, or are found wandering the forest fearfully bawling.

Imagine a small toddler with a huge mushroom shaped hat, perched upon its hair which is plaited into two pigtails. The hat shades a flat plate-like face with no features. Their feet are turned backwards so the toes align with the back of the calves. Its appearance at a glance can appear cute from afar, yet menacing up close.

This exceptionally grotesque description fascinates me, and I wanted to create the Dwen within a modern-day family. I also wanted to explore the thin barrier that exists between the world of the living and that of the dead, through our dreams.

Back home we are warned that our name is one of our most sacred possessions, and to 'take care' as it could be dangerous in the mouth of the wrong spirit. Many people describe incidences where they dreamt that a relative called their name or beckoned them, and remembered parents' and grandparents' warnings not to answer. Instead you should either: quote the 23rd psalm, yell – "I rebuke you, I rebuke", or encourage the voice/person to carry on their journey without you as it is believed if you answer the death summons you will never wake up.

The name-callers are normally relatives transitioning from life to death or who recently died. Scared, they roam the dreams of their living relatives and close friends seeking company. It then follows that you wake up to the news of this relative's death. Interestingly the moral of the Dwen story teaches young children not to answer their names if they cannot identify the caller's voice as it might be the Dwen attempting to lure the child away.

In Caribbean culture dreams can either be prophesy or premonition. It is believed that dreams of fishes mean that a close relative or friend is pregnant, while dreams of wedding dresses prophesies someone's imminent death.

One of my main preoccupations as a child was why the Dwen would hunt children? Once I began to research twins, the bonds that they form in the womb, and how this can be affected when the cord is severed, it began to make sense for the Dwen to have a twin. As losing a twin is described as being similar to a missing phantom limb.

Lastly, I really enjoyed trying to imagine the land of limbo. In Grenada the roots of the silk cotton tree are known for being the home for evil spirits. This ancient tree has huge roots with numerous cavernous spaces that are quite eerie and seemed the apt limbo environment for the Dwen.

*A Dictionary of Grenadian Creole English with Grammar & Syntax by Thomas R. Chase & Zarah Chase.

TIPHANIE

We children in Caribbean countries like Grenada and Trinidad grow up hearing stories about an elf-like spirit that lures children away from the land of the living. We are told if you hear a childlike voice calling your name do not follow it or you will disappear forever.

Dwens are mischievous spirits of children who died before being christened or given a name.

They:

>   are two to three feet tall, with feet turned backward,
>   wear mushroom-shaped straw hats over two long pigtails, and
>   have a flat plate-like face.

My name is Tiphanie Simmons and I will be telling you this story with the Baby-Dwen who sometimes gets things wrong.

Let me begin telling our tale:

The strange thing about being Caribbean is that our ancestors communicate with us through dreams. Adults know that you must not answer if you hear your name being called in your sleep, as it means a relative has just died and, afraid to take their death journey alone, is calling your name for you to accompany them. The strange thing is that when one person dies a new life begins and a baby will be born.

This tale begins on the night my father had such a dream:

Tonight, the air is hoarse in our home, a strangled picture we watch
muted, a single bedside lamp, our sparse spotlight to father's voice
straining, arms outstretched, muscles bulging against his white vest,
the King James Bible pressed against his chest

like a shield, muttering, *rebuke*, muttering, *get behind me …*,
to something we cannot see, tone tender but we feel the ripple
and wave of his voice, the tremors. His calm, *mama – go long you way,*
mama, leave me lone, you have stout walking shoes…

his litany rises to bellows, then falls to whispers,
and when the hissing begins, an acidic mist clogs our throats
and our eyes water as we stand at the threshold of our parents'
bedroom door, the sounds having disturbed our sleep too.

He is still sleeping, eyelids shut tight,
locked in the house of that dream
and we have no keys for that door, though our
mother tries.
She kneels in her pink nightgown
murmuring *hush, hush,*
hush up, palms patting then
stroking his back, to an
offbeat rhythm,

until at last, she begins to shake
him yelling, *don't answer your name if*
she calling you, you hear, shake shake, *I know is you mother but don't*
answer you hear, over and over, until our skin begins to raise
like prickly pineapples in the room's cool chill.

By the time the phone rings to announce my grandma's death
father is on the blue sofa drinking hot chocolate, dampening
the drama, denying he did any such superstitious nonsense,
while our mother kisses her teeth and is silent.

In my family we all know that dreaming of fishes means that someone is
pregnant. We knew that someone in our household was keeping secrets when
we all began to have the same dreams. Everyone would tell each other their
dreams except my mother and father. The longer they kept quiet the more
we began to suspect that they were going to be parents again. We excused
my father who we knew would give no credit to his dreams as he saw them as
superstitious nonsense. But we began to ambush my mother with renditions
of our dreams hoping that they would encourage her to confide in us.

Always my mother's mother sits across from her
hands folded across her chest, looks her in the eye, says,
you have something you want to tell me and always,
my mother shakes her head, with a little smile.

Always my father chuckles about all this superstitious nonsense,
*She too fast, she always feel say she know everything, always
fishing, but this time she wrong.* Mother shakes her head and smiles.

Always a few weeks later Aunty Lorraine visits and says,
*you have something to tell me cos I dream you swimming
in the little river by June Ann uncle's cousin Joe little wood shack,
just past the steep hill. The river rushing by fast fast
populated by gangs of fishes, swimming against the current, then two
leave the gangs and swim straight into your palms (now a little pond),
and they nibbling you fingers, slapping they fins against you palms, slapping,
slapping, like you-all clapping in harmony with the river-rhythm.*

Always the seven aunties visit to sit at the yellow kitchen table, their legs
crossed, or swinging, hands waving in chat about the latest dream of fishes –

and my father would always lean back his chair and laugh and laugh
and laugh – *she say fish jump into you hand and you never kill it,*
season it up good good and fry it – you all letting all of them
good good snappers go to waste, cheups man!

Always the day of the month that a young girl turns into a big woman,
always the night of the full moon, she too begins to dream
and so it was with me Tiphanie.

The next morning, I sit at that yellow table, legs crossed,
hands waving, telling my mother: *Mother I see you on a riverbank,*
sitting feet in the water, back hunched over, palms bracing you chin,
then next minute you in the bottom of the riverbank
two palm-sized fishes splayed across you chest as you hug them tight.
That is how I knew my mother was pregnant with twins.

DWEN-BABY

At last I can speak my part in this tale, my patience was being wrung tight
listening to Tiphanie chat. Wow that girl can chat for days. My part in this
story begins in the womb. I thought I was all alone you see. Well you cannot
imagine how scared I felt when I heard another heartbeat and realised there
was a brother in this womb with me. At first I did not know how to feel
realising too that:

We are half-moons in this womb's pond
expectant in this family's air. Our sister Tiphanie
hums to our mother's belly, while mother rubs
and father's deep voice greets us. We listen
to them while ruminating in an ocean of due dew,
the water tickling the skin of two commas curled
in warm translucent jelly – he is me,
We are the crick crack of broken mirrors – me is he
sitting, sipping brine, as we germinate in her bloated belly.

Yes, we this bouquet blossoming, jostling, weightless
as we sit still to listen with our ears, (our eyes not yet formed)
to our big sister Tiphanie Simmons singing, her voice fire and defiant in
a little house on Rock avenue.

It is amazing how Tiphanie sneaks into my part of the storytelling. Thank God
her part is brief. Well by six months my twin and I were interacting as well as
hearing and experiencing the rhythms of our mother's body and our expectant
family. We were naughty too so began to have a fine time:

Did I say sit still, no we slide and sway in our cozy water bubble.
Weight here is relative – outside this womb we can hear
and weigh the heft of our mother's lilting voice, measured
against the clink of cutlery, the bounce of the mattress, measured against our
two little brothers, Kojo and Kofi's footsteps stomping
floorboards until our mother hauls power up from her belly,
for deep bass (causing us to ripple) as she bellows – *STOP*,
STOP RUNNING, and in the sudden quiet, she says, – *all-yuh too hard ears*
voice so cold steel that we both flinch deep inside her blossoming
belly. We are a new language learning to read our world
with our ears while our skin soaks in wet dew.

Our father's voice rumbles, *chile wanti, wanti, cyan
getti and getti getti not wanti,* these evenings when Tiphanie
begs our mother's belly like ritual, to send two little sisters
to save her from all of these bothersome brothers, as father
jostles her out of the way to *nibble his little fishes,* he mutters
in this silly voice, lips tickling belly and mother's giggling, shakes
our water world. We feel this family's bloated berries of expectancy
ripen, and ferment as we swell.

It felt funny to chuckle whenever Tiphanie whispered her prayers for girls
ripe with the knowledge that we were twin boys. Sometimes I tried to speak,
well, really I tried to communicate with my brother. I like to feel that he could
hear me but was too shy to respond.

Brother do you know me?
shy creature sharing our birthing sack,
I say we cause, you feel like my second heart
beating,
I say we cause you feel like
one of my bones.
Hush now – I curl my arms round
you like a comma hugs
     a word, our bodies
       the pause
        between sentences.
        Brother do you feel like a we too?
         I say 'we' cause you feel like
        one of my bones.
        Brother do you feel like a
        we too?

By eight months we were a regular football team, we might not
have been able to speak to each other but I felt we knew each other's
thoughts and it felt so good to frolic and play so many games together:

Now our love bucks like an unbroken horse, flailing,
as the hooves strike our mother's ribs.
We mute munchkins eloquent in the slide and glide
of skin, the jabs and cuffs, collide and cuddle.

Each kick of my legs is half the weight of us, twin pearls
clammed in this translucent sack, even our shadows are sewn
tight with a binding stitch that cannot be unpicked. He breathes me, and I he.

We predict mother's stillness, by mapping
each stretched-out timeline
of stars, our watchful eyes
blanketing a dusky skyline,
by her stillness, and
the quiet, as we lay,
like she lays prone in
her bed, breathing in
time to the beat beat beat
of her heart. How we love
this quiet drumbeat of rest, to
be inert, our ears tuned to this static state.

Last night our toes blinked and tickled each other,
and I wonder did my twin's heart become bells in this pearl globe
the way mine tiptoed with each touch and how long we kept it up
rippling the dew nourishing us.

I am not going to lie to you, I could hear just how much pressure my sister
Tiphanie is under as the eldest child and began to make plans for the type of
brother that I would be. Don't tell her that I said that though:

Tiphanie, when I am born I will help/ I hear the daily soundscape of –
eldest / set example / mind you brothers / you are big sister / look after / look out for /
from Mother, from seven aunties, their husbands, and from father.
I hear this – litany / loop / echo / instruction / burden /
and know I will ease her life when she sings
to us in the belly, I want to say *big sister*
I will look out for / look after / shout at / my twin / yes him /
my other heartbeat / who will be the younger, as is this
not the way of older siblings?
I vowed this as the womb rocks her oval shape, humming
like a witnessing of this my solemn oath and we were pleased.
So it is I say to womb like sealing my oath, *so it is.*

Now we twins are a pair of dormant half-moons marinating in dew,
waiting for our due date so we can shine in our family's sky.

TIPHANIE
Dreams predict the future and I come from a long line of fortune tellers.
When we began to dream of wedding dresses, in my dreams two dresses
would hang from the ceiling then one would fall onto
A dusty floor and roll in the dirt. We knew that this did not bode well for
my mother's pregnancy as wedding dress means someone was going to
die in the near future: Somebody will _____ – A few months ago we
were dreaming fishes and now we were dreaming wedding dresses. O
dear somebody will _____

Me and my seven aunts seven aunts sit at the yellow kitchen

table kitchen table talking dreams where wedding dresses drag

drag filthy in stagnant water in stagnant water drag filthy filthy

talking of dreams where wedding dresses hang on rails hang

on rails drawing sunshine through louvres like magnets like

magnets but one dress is always in so much shadow so

much shadow the sun cannot touch it cannot touch it

and no hands wave no hands wave and each pair of feet

parked heavy on the wooden floor on the wooden floor

occasionally tap tap erratic taps erratic taps while father

pours hot water pours hot water from the whistling kettle

kettle humming humming a song about fishes about fishes

about fishes about fishes not asking what does this moody

mood mean mean mean not wanting to know to know what

what dreaming of wedding dresses wedding dresses means

means means only asking and asking and asking who is

getting married to who getting married to who not wanting

to involve himself in all these crazy women sitting at kitchen

table business not wanting to involve himself at all at all at all

Well our grandmother took each telling of another dream very hard indeed.
My mother ignored it all not wanting to acknowledge that one or both of
her babies might not make it, wanting to enter the birthing room with hope.
And our father kept muttering that this is all nonsense totally disbelieving
what he called superstitious claptrap since to dream of wedding dresses means
someone will die, and he did not want to believe that this meant one of the
babies in our mother's womb. But no matter how much we tried to ignore it,
the dreams of wedding dresses kept floating into our night sleep right up until
the night before my mother's waters broke. And I can tell you that by that
ninth month our worries were big rocks weighing our hearts and pebbles
rolling in our brains.

DWEN-BABY
There is turbulence, I hear *waters broke*, I hear *push push*
and I am swimming upstream in rough water.

Grandma is wailing, hollering bout wedding dresses, praying.
There are beeping sounds, voices, and mother is sobbing, then panting

I am about to make my exit when he, my twin sprawls across
the way blocking me and all I know is I should have been first.

Should have… then it is turbulent – the cord linking me and him unfurling
stretching, my neck choked, something squeezing neck, then pain

and it is turbulent, I hear the words *a boy*, then crying,
machines beeping fast fast, voices agitated, my neck

squeezed, I am alone in here now, there is no longer a we, there is no he,
and I feel my heart crack and the splinters juk my skin. I hear *push, push*

heart dropping, then *THEATRE NOW*, and mother's body is sliding, father's
voice straining, his deep hum, trembles.

Life cracked open and I was the egg who splattered,
into shadows, soon to become a hushed sound in the family's mouth.

TIPHANIE
I am not eloquent enough to describe the mood in our house when we bought
home one baby Kwaku to two cots set up for twins. I suppose I can only tell
you about the funeral for my little brother Kwame – who joined the shadows:

Today rain beats heavy on our umbrellas as we watch
them lower your coffin, no bigger than my Nike
shoebox, into soggy mud, the way Moses's mother must
have lowered his basket into the river by the rushes,
then set his big sister nearby to watch over him. But who
will watch over you little brother? My bowed head studies
the way the green grass stands next to the dried beige strand, like
the fate of my twin brothers. Two kiskadees dart about
in the raindrops, playing catch, like you must have done
with my brother in our mother's tummy. My feet and eyes
press into wet grass to avoid the lowering coffin as one
of the birds lands by my feet, abandoned by his brother,
his shadow is black against the pale wet sunlit canvas.
We are stretched tight like elastic bands from the sleepless
nights catering to your brother's cries. *He misses you,*
Grandma says, while I wonder who will warm you
under your blanket of heavy soil? Your christening
is a name etched on a gravestone, unlike Kwaku Simmons born
the right side of midnight on Tuesday. You Kwame Simmons slipped
into Wednesday, fore day morning already in the land of shadows
I watch the kiskadee cock his head over his yellow breast,
then take flight, and he seems to have lost his brother
here too. These days the sour taste of sadness lingers in our home,
a base scent mixing with our wonder over our new baby brother.

DWEN-BABY

When I first woke up I remembered nothing. Then I registered an emptiness
in the space next to me. I had never not felt my brother's presence and so began
to call for him *Brother where are you?* I tried speaking and speaking but he would
not answer with his body or his thoughts. Then I suddenly knew I was dead,
I was in the space between nighttime spice and morning dew. I was in the limbo
place between life and death. I remember the way that I kept reaching out for
my brother in this strange space. But he was missing. I tried speaking over and
over but he would not answer my calls. *Brother where are you?* This limbo space
is weird and I need you here with me:

I awake into a curdled fog spread around like custard. I awake
to the stench of fish gills and touch of gritty salted air.
The breeze feels like millions of sharp teeth, little fishes nibbling
my dead skin. This stagnant cavernous place, where ropes criss
cross the ceiling, filled in with a musky dusk. Here, spiders'
webs brush skin like damp cold wispy mist. Bats hang
from the ceiling ropes, hairy ugly beasts. And hanging beside
them – I squint at rows of grotesque toddlers, feet turned
backwards, flat plate faces, with eyes, but no lips
and a mushroom hat jammed fast onto their heads. My fear
becomes crawling crabs, claws pinching the insides of my belly.
I watch them swing then realise I am hanging too, so I must
be like them. How we hang there in sleep like soldiers,
a tumble down and go. How we drag, drag our backward
feet on the crispy earth, as we walk, feet shuffling
like hard board scraping crispy leaves, in this world
of in-between, this world of dead babies. This limbo world
under the silk cotton tree.

I soon realised that I had become a ghostly being, a warning parents give to their children. I had become a Dwen and that there are many different versions of me around the world, using different names:

Call me goblin, Little Rumpelstiltskin,
call me invisible friend
call me pot bellied
child ghost, better yet
call me bad mind,
call me ginal,
pied piper,
call me invisible
friend,
call me bogey man, better yet
call me devil spawn,
know I am the **Dwen**

who whispers
kids names
then lures
them astray.

It began with a missing, an absence for my brother, my missing limb. I made vows to him:

Brother I will find out you name / call you name.
Brother I will chant you name / and you will follow me
like scent you will / follow my whisper
follow my woop whoop / laughter.
Brother you name is a weapon / in my ghost mouth
a weapon / in my ghost mouth / me who died a shallow breath.
Brother come play hide and seek / with me.

And so I journeyed to the land of the living.

—

The sun flings herself against the concrete, stretching in the lazy evening. Dogs sprawl underneath the mouths of concrete houses during this ordinary day where lizards move with a slow sway. Ordinary day except that the Dwen has emerged from the shadows of the silk cotton tree seeking the name he needs to call. The name he needs to cure his hushed hurt. And when he finds it: Kwaku, the name for the missing half of his moon. He begins to call it in whispers like a rustling, like a scent you follow. That sound, that whoop, that child's laughter, like peeling bells, tolling softly. Like a whisper, he whispers *Kwaku – Kwaku –* chanting a litany, waiting waiting, his twin's name a weapon in his mouth. *Kwaku* luring his twin to his limbo land, under that Silk Cotton Tree.

ABOUT BEDTIME STORIES FOR THE END OF THE WORLD

Bedtime Stories for the End of the World explores the power of myth and the politics of storytelling. When civilisations fall, what's left behind is their ruins, their bones and their stories. In a world that seems on the brink of catastrophe, we ask what stories we want to preserve for future generations; sealing them up to protect them against rising waters, nuclear disaster, and the mundane tragedy of human forgetfulness. In 2017 we began a podcast series asking poets to pick a myth, legend or fairy story to reimagine for our age of crisis. We've seen fugitives and fire-thieves, Prometheus in a prison house and the Little Mermaid as a monstrous eco-warrior. We've encountered the Boo-Hags of the deep south, gods from the Norse and Hindu canons, King Arthur's Black Knight, the Green Man, the Vietnamese Warrior Triệu Thị Trinh, and the Irish giant-trickster Finn MacCumhaill. Described by BBC Radio 4 as "beautifully nerdy", the podcast has so far worked with 36 poets across two series, including Kei Miller, Andrew McMillan, Jay Bernard, Jack Underwood, Sabrina Mahfouz and many more.

We have run poetry events and workshops at the Southbank Centre, the Book Club and Poetry Society exploring contemporary takes on traditional stories.

Bedtime Stories for the End of the World is the brainchild of poet Eleanor Penny, and is produced by Tom MacAndrew.

endoftheworldpodcast.com

ELEANOR PENNY

Eleanor Penny is a writer, journalist, teacher, broadcaster and editor at Novara Media. She's a Barbican Young Poet, and winner of multiple national poetry competitions. Her poetry has been featured by The Poetry Society, Ambit Magazine, Verve Poetry and Three Drops. Her first collection is forthcoming from flipped eye. Her non-fiction appears in The New Statesman, The Independent, the London Review of Books and Verso Books. Her broadcast journalism and commentary regularly features on the BBC, Sky News, talkRADIO and LBC.

eleanorpenny.com

TOM MACANDREW

Tom MacAndrew is a freelance literature and spoken word producer. He has delivered projects for Forward Arts Foundation, Penned in the Margins, the Centre for Literacy in Primary Education, Poet in the City, Apples & Snakes, Poetry Translation Centre and Spread the Word.

He is the producer of Out-Spoken, London's largest monthly poetry night, and Out-Spoken Press; and has produced national and international tours, as well as education programmes, podcasts, radio shows, publications and events. He has developed projects with poets including Francesca Beard, Anthony Anaxagorou, Ella Frears, Joshua Idehen, John Hegley and Joelle Taylor.

tommacandrew.com

Inua Ellams

Ike/Rust

Born in Nigeria, Inua Ellams is a poet, playwright & performer, graphic artist & designer. He is a Complete Works poet alumni and facilitates workshops in creative writing where he explores reoccurring themes in his work – Identity, Displacement and Destiny – in accessible, enjoyable ways for participants of all ages and backgrounds.

His awards include: Edinburgh Fringe First Award 2009, the Liberty Human Rights Award, The Live Canon International Poetry Prize, The Kent & Sussex Poetry Competition, Magma Poetry Competition, Winchester Poetry Prize, an Arts Council of England Award, a Wellcome Trust Award, A Black British Theatre Award and The Hay Festival Medal for Poetry.

He has been commissioned by the Royal Shakespeare Company, National Theatre, Tate Modern, Louis Vuitton, Chris Ofili, BBC Radio & Television. His poetry books include *Thirteen Fairy Negro Tales* and *Candy Coated Unicorn and Converse* published by flipped eye, and *The Wire-Headed Heathen* by Akashic Books. His plays include *Black T-shirt Collection*, *The 14th Tale*, *Barber Shop Chronicles* and *Three Sisters* published by Oberon. He founded The Midnight Run (an arts-filled, night-time, urban walking experience), The Rhythm and Poetry Party (The R.A.P Party) which celebrates poetry & hip hop, and Poetry + Film / Hack (P+F/H) which celebrates Poetry & Film.

HELEN MORT

Voices from East of the Sun, West of the Moon

Helen Mort is a poet and novelist based in Sheffield. She is a five-times winner of the Foyle Young Poets of the Year award, received an Eric Gregory Award from The Society of Authors in 2007, and won the Manchester Poetry Prize Young Writer Prize in 2008.

Her first collection *Division Street* was published by Chatto & Windus in 2013 and was shortlisted for the Costa Book Awards and the T.S. Eliot Prize. Her second collection *No Map Could Show Them* was shortlisted for the Banff Mountain Literature Award in Canada.

She has published two pamphlets with Tall Lighthouse press. Helen's first novel *Black Car Burning* was published by Random House in April 2019 and she has also written short stories and drama (her play *Medusa* was performed by Proper Job Theatre in 2018).

In June 2018 Helen was elected as a Fellow of the Royal Society of Literature. She lectures in creative writing at Manchester Metropolitan University. She is currently working on her first non-fiction project, a book about motherhood and mountaineering.

JOELLE TAYLOR

A Bluebeard Among The Blue Birds

Joelle Taylor is an award-winning poet, playwright and author who has recently completed touring Europe, Australia, Brazil and South East Asia with her latest collection *Songs My Enemy Taught Me*. She is widely anthologised, the author of three full poetry collections and three plays and is currently completing her debut book of short stories *The Night Alphabet*.

Her new collection *Butterfly Fist* will be published in June 2021, and she is developing a spoken word theatre show of the script that will tour throughout the year.

She has featured on radio and television including The Verb (Radio 3), Power Line, Poetry Please (Radio 4), Educating the East End (ITV), and We Belong Here (BBC). She presented a Radio 4 documentary about her art and life, which was broadcast in May 2020.

Joelle founded SLAMbassadors, the UK's national youth slam championships, for the Poetry Society in 2001 and was its Artistic Director and National Coach until 2018. Her work is taught as part of the OCR GCSE syllabus, and she has received a Change Maker Award from the Southbank Centre in recognition of the effect SLAMbassadors had on British culture. She also founded the inter-European spoken word project 'Borderlines', which links communities of spoken word artists together across the UK & Europe.

She is the host and co-curator of Out-Spoken, the UK's premier poetry and music club, currently resident at the Southbank Centre, London.

KAYO CHINGONYI

Nyaminyami

Kayo Chingonyi's debut collection, *Kumukanda* (Chatto & Windus, 2017) was a Guardian and Telegraph Book of the Year, and the winner of the 2018 International Dylan Thomas Prize and a Somerset Maugham Award.

A former Burgess Fellow at the Centre for New Writing, University of Manchester, and Associate Poet at The Institute of Contemporary Arts, London, Kayo is now Poetry Editor for The White Review, and an Assistant Professor in the Department of English Studies at Durham University. He has performed his work at festivals and events around the world. *A Blood Condition*, a new collection of poems, will be published by Chatto & Windus, and his memoir *Prodigal*, is forthcoming with Picador.

WILL HARRIS

Moon Station 5

Will Harris is a writer of Chinese Indonesian and British heritage, born and based in London. He works in schools, leads workshops and teaches occasionally.

A selection of his work can be found in the Bloodaxe anthology *Ten: Poets of the New Generation*. He is also the author of a short book about race, masculinity and heroism called *Mixed-Race Superman* (Peninsula Press, 2018). He has been featured on Poetry International and in ES Magazine as part of the "new guard" of London poets. His favourite poem is this Martin West translation of Sappho's fragment 96: "there… this… mind… much… sings…". His favourite quotation is from *The Unquiet Grave*, where Palinurus says: "the child who fears noises becomes the man who hates them". His favourite film is an earnest art house film from the early-90s called *Dumb and Dumber*. His first full poetry collection, *RENDANG*, was published by Granta in 2020.

MALIKA BOOKER

The Making of a Dwen

Malika Booker is a British poet and theatre maker of Guyanese and Grenadian parentage, and the founder of the writers collective, Malika's Poetry Kitchen. Her pamphlet *Breadfruit*, (flipped eye, 2007) received a Poetry Book Society recommendation and her poetry collection *Pepper Seed* (Peepal Tree Press, 2013) was shortlisted for the OCM Bocas prize and the Seamus Heaney Centre 2014 prize for first full collection.

She is published with the poets Sharon Olds and Warsan Shire in *Penguin Modern Poets 3: Your Family, Your Body* (2017) and her poem 'Nine Nights', first published in The Poetry Review in autumn 2016, was shortlisted for Best Single Poem in the 2017 Forward Prizes.

Malika received her MA from Goldsmiths University and has recently begun a PhD at the University of Newcastle. She was the Douglas Caster Cultural Fellow in Creative Writing at Leeds University, the inaugural Poet in Residence at The Royal Shakespeare Company and the first British poet to be a fellow at Cave Canem. In 2020 Booker received a Cholmondeley Award for outstanding contribution to poetry.

Malika hosts and curates New Caribbean Voices, Peepal Tree Press's literary podcast, and is currently a Lecturer in Creative Writing at Manchester Metropolitan University.

INKQUISITIVE (AMANDEEP SINGH)

Inkquisitive, aka Amandeep Singh, is a world-renowned artist and illustrator. His work engages with religion, politics and hip-hop.

Inkquisitive believes art should express freedom and is a form of visual poetry. His work is owned, has been commissioned by and is recognized by many celebrities including Drake, J Cole, Madhuri Dixit, Jennifer Lopez, P Diddy, Stormzy, The Weeknd and LL Cool J. Amandeep has also worked with prominent brands including Apple, Warner Brothers and River Island.

Inkquisitive's father is a calligrapher who worked for the High Commission of India and often completed work for the royal family and various prime ministers. It was watching his father practising his art that first encouraged Inkquisitive to pick up a pen.

He was one of the first artists to use contemporary social media to develop his profile. Aman began posting on Facebook under the moniker Inkquisitive in 2010 - the name was gifted to him by his mother - and quickly gained 20,000 followers. He landed his first solo exhibition in Canada in 2012 and has grown his fan base exponentially since then. Following a further 24 solo exhibitions around the globe, he has built an engaged social media following of close to half a million.

Inkquisitive's passion for promoting social cohesion and community activism is evident in his diverse network of supporters around the globe.